THE PERMACULTURE GARDENING BIBLE: A COMPREHENSIVE PRACTICAL GUIDE TO BUILDING A SUSTAINABLE, SELF-SUFFICIENT ORGANIC GARDEN

DEVELOP HIGH EFFICIENCY SEED, WATER, SOIL, SHELTER AND ENERGY SYSTEMS FOR ORGANIC NATURAL GARDEN GROWTH IN YOUR BACKYARD

DAVID WHITEHEAD

SILK PUBLISHING

CONTENTS

INTRODUCTION

The permaculture idea promotes a healthy, sustainable way of life. Simply said, permaculture cooperates with nature rather than fighting it. Ecosystems in the wild are self-regenerating and self-sustaining. Practitioners of permaculture observe these organic processes and mimic them in their gardens or backyards.

It addresses how to develop communities, build housing, and raise food, all while reducing the environmental effect. People all around the world are continually advancing and perfecting its concepts in a variety of climatic and cultural settings.

In permaculture gardens, the best elements of native plant cultivation, edible landscaping, and wildlife gardening are combined into a low-maintenance, self-sufficient, and productive ecosystem.

Permaculture gardens provide a variety of uses. Permaculture gardens use a range of applications rather than restricting the garden to just one. A permaculture garden offers year-round food and medicinal crops, wildlife habitats, handicraft supplies, a lovely appearance, and a quiet, peaceful setting.

Introduction

In this book, you are going to learn more about the concept of permaculture and how you can perfect permaculture gardening. This book combines all the necessary info needed to equip you with the best possible details about permaculture. The book ensures that after going through it, you will find that beginning your own permaculture gardening will be an easy task.

CHAPTER 1
WHAT IS PERMACULTURE?

Is there anyone who doesn't want to grow more food in a shorter period of time and at less cost? What permaculture provides is exactly what you're looking for. The permaculture gardener does not rely on chemical fertilizers, herbicides, or pesticides; instead, he or she uses natural methods to improve the soil, suppress weeds, and encourage plant growth while reusing the garden's waste. Growth your own food can be intimidating for someone who has never done it before, but permaculture offers design tools and growing practices that make it easier to produce more food for your loved ones while also reducing the amount of time you spend in the garden.

When Bill Mollison and David Holmgren formalized permaculture in Australia in the late 1970s, they combined sustainable agriculture, landscape design, and ecology into a single system (the name is drawn from the terms permanent agriculture and permanent culture). Home gardeners are encouraged to work with nature rather than against it, and this method encourages them to do so. Hugelkultur, fruit tree guilds, and the food forest are all themes that can easily be incorporated into any edible garden.

Organic gardening and permaculture have a lot in common, yet the latter takes a different approach. Because natural ecosystems serve as a model, plants are clustered together in plant communities that benefit one another. Gardeners that practice permaculture prioritizes perennials over annuals and plant a variety of crops on the same site at the same time. Water harvesting is just one example of continuing recycling and re-use operations in the garden. Soil development through no-till methods is also advocated by permaculture, which does not support plowing and digging the soil.

The philosophy of Masanobu Fukuoka had a significant impact on the forefathers of permaculture. Do-nothing farming was invented by Fukuoka, an agricultural scientist who returned to his family farm after giving up his career as a researcher. First, he said, "What do you not have the ability to do?" Chemical fertilizers and pesticides aren't necessary because this method of farming doesn't rely on the plow to turn the soil. When it comes to pest control, it relies on biological systems like beneficial insects and cover crops.

Using Fukuoka's concept, perennial white Dutch clover and grain crops such as barley, rice, and wheat are rotated in the fields. Clay and compost are mixed with seeds to make balls, which are then sown in the fields. After harvesting the grain, the straw is used as mulch for the following crop. In One Straw Revolution, Fukuoka explains his methods and beliefs. "If we toss Mother Nature out the window, she comes back in the door with a pitchfork" is one of my favorite Fukuoka quotes.

THE HISTORY

In 1974, millions of teenagers around the world began to question the way we live today. Back-to-the-land movements, communes, and hippies appeared all over the world during the 1960s and 1970s. When David Holmgren was a final-year student at the University of Tasmania in Australia, he met Bill Mollison, a lecturer who shared his interest in ecological and human systems. David authored a thesis on how he thought the world should operate in the wake of discussions with Bill and his own experiences in the gardens and fields of Tasmania. Ecosystems, human settlements, and agriculture were all intertwined in an innovative design concept. David's graduate thesis included the manuscript, but more crucially, Bill urged him to publicize his ideas. In 1978, the book Permaculture One was published as a result of the thesis. Mollison and Holmgren took their cue from Russell Smith's Tree Crops: A Permanent Agriculture (1924), but the term permaculture has since expanded to encompass much more than just sustainable agriculture.

Permaculture became a major focus for Bill Mollison after the book's success. According to him, permaculture is the "harmonious integration of the landscape with people and appropriate technologies" that provides "food," "shelter," "energy," "and all other material and non-material needs in a sustainable way."

Modern permaculture has taken on various meanings. An entire manner of life has been detailed. A way of life. A way of thinking. Permaculture, at its core, is a technique of designing all human systems in a way that is harmonious with the natural world. Everything from community systems to cultural beliefs to commercial practices to art has been influenced by it. Because the concept extended far beyond agriculture, what was originally dubbed "permanent agriculture" came to be known as "permanent culture."

"While providing an abundance of food, fiber and energy for local needs, these landscapes are created in a way that mimics nature's patterns and interactions" is how David Holmgren characterized permaculture. Toby Hemenway, a legendary permaculture teacher, put it this way: "Turn every burden into an asset."

The publication of "Permaculture One" led to Mollison being called to lecture at a number of educational institutions about his and Holmgren's innovative ideas. Unfortunately, he soon discovered that he was merely being called to these prestigious institutions in order to dispute and dissect permaculture, and he left disappointed with higher education. The Permaculture Research Institute and an experimental farm in Australia were established in response to this. A certification program was developed as the movement gained momentum. Mollison attempted to trademark the term "permaculture" at one point but was unsuccessful; he did, however, succeed in copyrighting the term for educational use. They must take the PDC from someone who has one in order to get a Permaculture Design Certificate.

No longer is there a list of teachers that the organization keeps up to date. To continue with permaculture education, both Mollison and Holmgren disagreed. When it came to curriculum, Mollison wanted to retain total control and keep it strictly scientific, but Holmgren wanted to give the teachers total freedom and allow for religious instruction. Both possibilities came to fruition in the end.

Individuals have complete control over the content of their education and can make their own decisions about what they learn. The difficulty of finding an experienced and knowledgeable permaculture teacher is due to this; however, as Mollison said in his book "Travels in Dreams" (1996): "Finally, with hundreds of itinerant teachers turning up wherever, the system is beyond restraint. Safe at long last and growing geometrically—we have triumphed! "Permaculture is indefensible," says the author.

PERMACULTURE AND FOOD

First and foremost, I learned how to cultivate from my mom. When I was a kid, I recall her tending vegetable patches outside the front porch and in several community gardens as well. Having grown up around veggies, I have a newfound respect for the wide range of options available to us, both in the garden and on our plates. Nothing beats a home-cooked meal made with ingredients you just plucked from the garden moments before you sat down to dine. Fresh food is not only more flavorful, but it is also healthier for you nutritionally.

Edible gardeners and permaculture go hand in hand because permaculture not only produces a more sustainable and responsible garden and community but it also produces a lot of delicious food. Soil preparation, watering, and weed control are all critical to successful edible gardening. Plant selection and timing are also important. When it comes to meeting these demands, permaculture is an excellent option because it requires just minimal time and money. Because gardening in methods that enrich rather than deplete the garden's resources is the best long-term answer to producing an abundance of food.

Permaculture begins with a well-designed garden. Landscaping typical of a home with a huge lawn and vegetable plots off to the side is inefficient and requires a lot of work to maintain. To make the most of every available growing surface, such as backyards, front yards, curb strips, decks, balconies, fire escapes, rooftops, walls and fencing, adjacent yards, and community and school gardens, permaculture makes use of practices adapted from indigenous peoples all over the world. Using these techniques, I have found that they help increase the amount of food that can be grown in a given area. It is possible to increase your growing space by using permaculture techniques in cold climates, such as cold frames, hoop buildings, and greenhouses to start seedlings indoors. Permaculture can be used in hot locations to generate shade and capture water.

If earlier generations have left the soil in an unhealthy state, permaculture has a solution for even the most depleted soils. Dirt is the foundation of all successful gardening. You can't develop robust and hardy plants if you don't have healthy, diversified soil. Gardeners who use permaculture instead of conventional farming and gardening cultivate their soils in ways that imitate the natural food web in the soil.

Last but not least, in permaculture, eating what grows well in your area and savoring the season are fundamental principles. Getting an orange in your Christmas stocking used to be a huge deal for baby boomers. That's because oranges were exclusively cultivated in Florida and California, and they were pricey and exotic. We've lost a connection to local farmers and food because so much of our food is now shipped across the country on a regular basis. We are encouraged by permaculture to support our local farmers by eating seasonally appropriate food and conserving and sharing the harvest. For our own gardens, we employ a wide variety of plants dependent on the space and the individuals who will be caring for them.

Is permaculture only about cultivating plants? Not if you want to get the most out of it. Reconnecting ourselves to our agricultural roots is the goal of this ethical method of cultivating food. As a newer system, it is founded on cultural practices that have been replaced by industrial agriculture and fast food. Permaculture is a cutting-edge, ten-thousand-year-old technology that teaches us how to cultivate food sustainably.

Embracing both traditional pre-industrial agricultural and cultural influences from other countries and regions is one of the most appealing aspects of permaculture design. In this way, we return to the idea of small-scale farming, when resources were shared amongst the community, and the garden itself was a part of the ecosystem.

THE PERMACULTURE ETHICS

The three ethical pillars of permaculture are: caring for the earth, caring for other people, and sharing plenty, all of which are intertwined (fair share). In many traditional cultures, the interests of all members of the group are taken into account, as well as the interests of the entire community and of the planet.

Earth Care

The living soil food chain is crucial to all life, including our own, according to the principles of Earth care. According to David Holmgren, "The state of the soil is typically the best metric for the health and well-being of society. The greatest way to detect if the soil is healthy is to see how much life there is. There are many different ways to look after the soil. It's considerably more difficult to grow a lot of food if your soil isn't healthy. Respect and appreciation for the planet's woods, grasslands and waterways, as well as the variety of species they support, is also critical. Permaculture ethics begin by acknowledging the interconnection of life.

People Care

Taking care of yourself and spreading that care to your family, friends, and community is the first step toward caring for others. It is possible to cultivate food for ourselves and our families, but it is also possible for gardeners to give back to the community.

Fair Share

Social activists and gardeners in my family have taught me about the significance of caring for the environment and for others. To be able to give freely to others, we must believe that we have enough of our own needs met. However, it isn't required to raise every imaginable crop in order to create abundance. If we can cultivate our own food, we should do so and then locate other gardeners to trade with. Even if we don't have the ability or desire to raise every crop, we can still enjoy a wide variety of foods thanks to this method.

PERMACULTURE'S TWELVE ESSENTIAL PRINCIPLES

It is important to note that permaculture varies from conventional gardening approaches in that it is a way of thinking and reacting to a certain ecology. Because no two gardens, families, or communities are the same, permaculture must rely on observation and local expertise to succeed. There are twelve guiding principles in permaculture, in addition to the fundamental ideas of planet care, people care, and fair sharing. Permaculture design concepts can be applied to any type of garden, whether you are establishing a new one or modifying an existing one.

1. Observe and interact

A thorough awareness of your site and local conditions is essential to a successful permaculture endeavor. If you want to acquire a thorough picture of your site, you need to spend a year there, monitoring everything from sun, rain, snow, animals, and scenery. Even if you don't have access to land, you can see what grows best in your area by looking at neighboring gardens.

2. Catch and store energy

Summertime squirrels gather nuts to keep them going during the long, cold winter, and the permaculture notion of harvesting and storing energy is a lot like that. When resources are plentiful, there are numerous methods for catching and preserving them so that you can use them later when they are scarce. Plants can be kept warm by using a greenhouse to store solar energy. A greenhouse can even provide passive solar heat for neighboring buildings if it is placed in the right location. Food energy can be stored by canning summer fruits and vegetables for the upcoming winter months. In the dry months, harvesting rainwater or recycling greywater from the house protects valuable irrigation water from being wasted to runoff or the sewage system and produces water energy during the dry season

3. Obtain a yield

All edible gardens are designed to produce food. Permaculture delivers other less tangible but no less valuable benefits. The exchange of knowledge or talents amongst gardeners can provide a profit. In community gardens, neighbors labor together to build raised beds, tool huts, fences, and trellises, as well as mulch walks. Experienced gardeners can share their knowledge and skills with the next generation through school gardens. As a community, we may learn from one another.

4. Apply self-regulation and respond to feedback

My understanding of Native American philosophy has always been that the phrase "Think of Seven Generations" refers to thinking about the future seven generations in advance. My experience has taught me that also includes thinking about our own great-grandparents and grandparents and parents and ourselves as well as the future generations we hope to have in mind.

There are two strategies to ensure that our future generations can profit from all of our hard work in the garden: annual planting and soil improvement. The first is to treat our garden as if it were a continuous system, beginning with respect for the previous generations' efforts at land stewardship. Our own mistakes or those of our forefathers can also be remedied when we respond to feedback. This could include replanting portions of the garden that haven't been productive or improving soil that has become depleted.

5. Make use of renewable resources.

Examples of renewable multipurpose resources are trees. Fruit, nuts, seeds, building materials, and fuel are all derived from them. During the summer, they provide shade for cooling our homes, preventing the wind from blowing, filtering the air, and releasing the oxygen that we need. Fruit trees can be a dependable source of food for future generations if we follow the principle of fair sharing. The wood from rotting trees can be used to build new beds, grow mushrooms, or make mulch, knowing that all decomposing wood will eventually be incorporated into the soil as it decays.

6. Produce no waste

There's no waste in a permaculture garden since everything grows. Instead, we look for creative methods to repurpose the produce we harvest from our garden. Garden critters, like red worms, efficiently convert organic wastes like food scraps into soil additives, which are subsequently reintroduced into the garden's vegetable beds as compost. Compost tea is made from the castings produced by the worms' digestive systems, which enrich the soil food web. An edible plant's life cycle, from harvest to kitchen scraps to worm castings, is shown here in its entirety.

7. Design from pattern to details

Learning from nature's patterns and applying them to your own life is the purpose of permaculture. Everything from galaxies to the structure of DNA and even the garden snail has a spiral shape. It's a good design template for a herb garden because it maximizes the usage of a small space. To create microclimates, you can utilize certain plants to shade others in a spiral-shaped bed. As a result, plants that prefer the shade, like mint and violets, can be grown alongside herbs that prefer the sun, like rosemary and thyme.

8. Integrate rather than segregate

Plants that are placed in the correct combinations work together rather than compete with one another to thrive. Thus, the garden as a whole becomes more than the sum of its individual components. In addition, when you take the time to analyze an existing landscape, you may then identify ways to make improvements so that all of the features function in harmony.

9. Use small and slow solutions

A quick remedy or an immediate payoff is not the goal in permaculture. Each component of a garden system should contribute to the overall garden function over time, and this is the goal of creating an intricate garden system. An example of this is a focus on long-lived crops like wheat. Perennials save water and disturb less soil because they don't need to be replanted every year.

It may take a while for perennials like chicory and sorrel to begin producing because they are among the first to emerge in colder locations. Permaculture, on the other hand, emphasizes small-scale, local solutions above large-scale, industrial ones. All of these little and gradual solutions are instances of backyard sharing, local produce swaps, community gardens, and regional seed libraries.

10. Use and value diversity

Most gardeners enjoy perusing plant catalogs in search of new varieties of veggies to cultivate, and this variety isn't only interesting, it's also clever. Diverse crops, whether on a farm or in a backyard garden, are more resistant to a single disease or insect when planted close together. During the Potato Famine, which lasted from 1845 to 1852, as many as one million people died, and a similar number emigrated from Ireland. Potatoes have been planted and developed in the Andean region for more than 5000 years, and there are dozens of different types to choose from. A permaculture garden should include a mix of new and familiar species each year. If you have a wide variety of plants to pick from, your garden will be less susceptible to damage from setbacks. Climate change and other environmental threats necessitate this kind of preparedness.

11. Use the edges

All of the available space is maximized in a permaculture garden. This may entail constructing flowerbeds, herb gardens, and vegetable gardens with a variety of unique shapes. Keyhole beds, for example, are based on the design of an antique keyhole. A garden mandala consists of a series of keyhole beds arranged around each other. In a circle of six keyhole beds, one way serves as the entry and a circular region in the center serves as a turning area. As a result, more plantable acreage is gained while minimizing the amount of path space required.

12. Creatively use and respond to change

In the garden, it's impossible to predict what will happen next. What's successful one year could not be the best the next. One of the most crucial skills for the permaculture gardener is adaptability in the face of environmental changes. Rather than attempting to tamper with nature, our purpose is to work with it. Keeping this notion in mind will help you deal with the difficulties that come with cultivating edibles. In the garden, there are no failures, simply lessons that help you get there.

CHAPTER 2
THE BASICS OF PERMACULTURE

THE POLYCULTURE GARDEN

Permaculture relies heavily on fruit tree guilds and food forests. Which of these terms is correct? It was common for pre-industrial European societies to be organized into guilds, each devoted to a specific trade. There are no competing plants in permaculture guilds because they are arranged around fruit or nut trees. It's important to remember that in permaculture, we combine rather than separate, creating interdependent systems. We're working to create plant combinations that reduce the number of time gardeners have to spend weeding and maintaining their plots. Because guilds are not present in nature, they cannot be referred to be native plants. Guilds, on the other hand, are rooted in nature.

When a variety of plants are grown together, they form mutually beneficial partnerships. The three sisters, a Native American polyculture of three plants, is the most well-known polyculture model. Squash covers the ground to keep weeds at bay and conserve moisture, while corn gives support for beans that fix nitrogen in the soil. Single crops like bananas or blueberries are produced on hundreds of thousands of acres in monocultures. Lasers are used to ensure that strawberry fields are perfectly flat. In the Midwest, vast swaths of prairie have been transformed into fields of wheat, corn, or soy. Fertilizers, herbicides, and insecticides are all examples of chemicals that are required.

As a result, enormous amounts of human and technological energy are expended. Monocultures, according to Bill Mollison, are perpetuated disorders. As a result, polyculture provides more flowers and herbs, more helpful insects, fewer pests, less work and less space, higher yields and more resilience to varying temperatures and rain. Only a problem arises when you have too many tomatoes in your edible permaculture garden: what to do with them all?

Permaculturists try to grow as many diverse types of food and beneficial plants as possible, which is a form of diversification. Each of my garden beds has at least twelve to fifteen different kinds of vegetables. A variety of plants can offer sustenance even if some crops fail. They may nibble on lettuce and sunflower sprouts, but not much of the spicy mustard greens or tomatoes. Slugs could consume all of our lettuce if we simply planted it. Slugs won't consume the vegetables we've interplanted, so we're guaranteed a crop.

When it comes to the edible food forest, we develop guilds that function much like natural mixed species ecosystems, with all the elements working together to produce biodiverse polyculture.

FRUIT TREE GUILDS

In a guild, a fruit or nut tree serves as the centerpiece. Most edible fruit and nut trees are deciduous; therefore, it is easier to construct guilds with deciduous trees because when the leaves fall, you may plant cool-season crops underneath. There are many more uses for evergreen trees in bigger gardens, such as windbreaks or shade. To sustain the central tree, various plant communities are arranged in concentric circles, with each community serving a specific function such as nitrogen fixation, mulching, searching for nutrients, and attracting beneficial insects.

Each region has its own unique set of needs; therefore, tree guilds come up with novel pairings to meet those needs. With the help of the guild system, you may construct a food forest that is tailored to your own needs and climate. A well-functioning food forest can aid in a variety of gardening tasks, including delivering nutrients to the soil, eliminating weeds, and promoting beneficial insects. Always remember that permaculture's ultimate purpose is to produce more food with less effort.

Nitrogen Fixers

Soil bacteria and certain plant roots create a symbiotic interaction to fix atmospheric nitrogen (N) in the roots of nitrogen-fixing plants. Plants cannot develop without nitrogen, plain and simple. Despite the fact that nitrogen is an important component of existence, we and all other creatures and plants are unable to directly absorb nitrogen from the environment. Nature, on the other hand, has an answer. Legumes such as peas and beans have developed to serve as food sources for the microorganisms that inhabit their roots, but legumes aren't the only legumes that do this. For their part, the bacteria fix atmospheric nitrogen, which the roots can then utilize physiologically. The nitrogen in plants is converted into proteins, enzymes, and amino acids that are then ingested by animals and humans farther up the food chain. So, in addition to providing nitrogen to fuel plant growth, the planting of nitrogen-fixing legumes establishes a crucial nutritional system.

An excellent supporting layer for the guild would be small trees and shrubs in the legume family. It is not necessary to replace these plants each year because they add additional nitrogen to the soil and are perpetual. Several nitrogen-fixing trees and shrubs, such as acacias, agastaches, alder, lupins, locusts, mesquites, the Siberian peashrub (Caragana arborescens), seaberries (Hippophae rhamnoides), and tagasaste, can be pruned or coppiced (Chamaecytisus palmensis).

Trimmings and branches should be left as mulch in their original locations. As a result of the pruning, the trees die back and release the nitrogen and organic stuff that they had been storing.

Living Mulches

The fruit and nut tree guild's next biggest supporter is mulch. Mulch is a thick covering of organic material applied to the soil to protect it against weeds and erosion. Mulch prevents weeds from growing, keeps the soil moist, and gradually improves soil fertility over time. Mulch production on-site saves both time and money because you don't need to import resources from an outside source.

It is common knowledge that gardeners use a variety of mulches, from straw to woodchips to plastic sheets. A notable example of zero-waste production is cut-and-come-again plants, which provide the ideal mulch for a supporting layer in the tree guild. When clipped several times over the season, vigorous herbaceous perennials like comfrey will produce new leaves. Comfrey in my garden provides me with a dozen or more cuts each year.

Trimmed leaves are either buried under mulch or made into liquid fertilizer by simmering them. Sunchokes (Jerusalem artichokes) are also used as mulch in my garden. These 15-foot-tall huge perennial sunflowers are vigorous enough to be pruned back several times during the growing season while still producing a substantial supply of edible tubers in the winter.

Squash, pumpkins, and other large-leafed annuals, such as these, can also act as living mulches, spreading swiftly and shading the ground. Mulch will quickly take over a small garden if you don't use a compact shrub variety like 'Table Queen.'

Nutrient Catchers

Dynamic nutrient accumulators are the next group of fruit and nut tree supports. Plants also require micronutrients like calcium, iron, and magnesium in addition to macronutrients like nitrogen, phosphorus, and potassium. Those plants with lengthy taproots, known as nutrient catchers, go deep into the soil to find these micronutrients and bring them back to the surface for other plants. The majority of accumulators target a specific nutrient shortage in the soil and can be utilized to address it.

Chicory, dandelion, and yellow dock are examples of weeds in this group. In addition to serving as food for other plants in the guild, they can be eaten as tender spring greens and then cut back in the summer to be used as mulch or composted. Borage, lupines, marigolds, and yarrow are just a few of the popular flowers that are known for their ability to store nutrients.

Insect Attractors

Last but not least, the fruit and nut tree guild can rely on the support of insectary plants. Pest predators and pollinators are the most likely targets of gardeners' suspicions when it comes to insects in the vegetable patch, yet entomologists estimate that just 10% of common garden bugs are pests that harm crops. Predators can reduce the number of pests that harm our plants while pollinating them, which is critical for the production of fruit and seed crops. An insect population that is well-balanced is fostered in a food forest, which is a type of wildlife habitat. Insect predators like birds and bats, which can consume pests like beetles, caterpillars, and mosquitoes, are drawn to the area because of this.

Mustard, carrot, aster, and are among of the most commonly consumed insects in the insectary. Pollen and nectar are readily available to parasitic wasps and flies if they are not collected or pinched back when they are not harvested or pinched back. These beneficial insects may go on to eat pests or use them as incubators for their progeny, depending on how they've been introduced. Onion and mint plants are also deserving of honorable attention.

FOOD FORESTS

To a certain extent, food forests and edible forest gardens build on the idea of fruit tree guilds on a smaller scale. The mushroom layer and vines that crawl across the strata are examples of the many different types of plants that can be found in a forest, starting with the dense canopy of large trees and moving down to smaller trees, shrubs, herbs, and ground covers. David Holmgren observed that in order to maximize the use of resources like soil, water, and sunlight, we must design from patterns in nature and stack plants in layers.

The foundation of the garden is the tall tree layer, like a tree is the heart of a guild. In a common configuration, the north side of the garden is planted with large trees, and the south side is planted with smaller trees in decreasing layers such that no layer is shaded by the one below it. Long-lived nut trees like Korean pine (Pinus koreana) and fruit trees such as apples, pears, and plums on non-dwarfing rootstocks are examples of ideal trees for this stratum. This stratum of tall trees may be home to squirrels, which may be able to get seeds and nuts. There are raptors that perch in the trees that can assist you with rodent control, such as falcons, hawks, and owls.

Fruit trees on semi-dwarf rootstock can be found in the small tree layer, which normally grows between 12 and 20 feet tall. It's possible to find them in the form of a wide variety of fruits and nuts. Coppicing (frequently chopping down to the ground) nitrogen fixers like alder in cold-winter regions can help (Alnus species). Acacia species, carob (Ceratonia siliqua), mimosa (Albizia julibrissin), and white lead tree are good nitrogen-fixing tiny trees that can be frequently coppiced in moderate winter locations (Leucaena leucocephala). Insects that prey on other plants may attract birds to the small tree layer, where they can raise their young.

FOOD FOREST LAYERS

Food forests have eight basic layers: the tall tree layer or canopy, the small tree layer, the shrub layer, the herb or herbaceous layer, the root layer, the ground cover layer, vines, and mushrooms.

Bamboo

Depending on the species, bamboos are woody perennial grasses that can be found in a variety of habitats across the food forest. However, some can reach a height of 50 feet or more, making it evident that they belong in the layer of big trees rather than the shrub layer.

A genuine permaculture plant, bamboo thrives in soil rich in organic matter. Its quick expansion allows for accurate and timely screening. Additionally, bamboo is a significant source of food and refuge for birds because of its amazing beauty and minimal vulnerability to illness or pests. Plant stakes, trellises, arbors, and fences can all be constructed from sturdy culms or poles. Building a clothesline, coop for chickens, an outdoor shower, and entry gate have all been done with bamboo poles I've purchased. Mulch is formed by the decomposition of plant leaves. Finally, the young shoots can be consumed.

Runners and clumpers are the two main types of bamboo. Bamboo's reputation as an invasive species has been tarnished by its runners. In milder regions, clumping plants have a different growth pattern and don't overstep their limitations. Selecting the right species and planting it appropriately will help you avoid a lot of problems with bamboo. P. nigra and P.nigra "Henon" are two of my favorite black bamboo runners, as well as P. nigra nude sheath bamboo for the coldest climates (P. nuda). Big timber, Buddha belly, Alfonse Karr, and Chusquea gigantea, a strong core bamboo, are among my favorite clumpers.

Make sure the planting area has 4 to 5 inches of well-rotted horse dung and homemade compost before adding an additional 6 to 12 inches of mulch. Runners necessitate a large amount of room for their activities. While they can be kept under control in cold or dry climates, digging a trench and installing a plastic rhizome barrier that is 30 to 36 inches deep is required elsewhere. The key here is to avoid burying the barrier too far beneath the compost and mulch layers. The bamboo will be able to cross the barrier if you do so. As a general rule, I prefer to keep 2 inches of rhizome barrier above the mulch so that I can easily identify and remove any rhizomes that are trying to escape.

Watering must be done on a regular basis. Using a sharp knife, remove the new shoots from the bamboo plants by digging through their mulch and compost. Peel and boil the bamboo shoots for twenty-five minutes, then stir-fry them. At different periods of the year, different species of plants will grow new branches.

Individual culms need to harden for three to four years before being used in garden construction. The remarkable thing about bamboo is that you can harvest a third of its biomass annually after three years without harming the plant in any way. Every year, thin out the bamboo stands even if you don't need the poles to keep the grove accessible.

Currants, highbush blueberries, elderberries, huckleberries, goumi (Elaeagnus multiflora), gooseberries, sea buckthorn (Hippophae species), and serviceberries can all be found in the shrub layer (Amelanchier species). If you live somewhere with cold winters, you may benefit from planting hazelnuts and filberts (Corylus species) as understory shrubs because they can tolerate moderate shadow. Many of these plants are also extremely beautiful, and nitrogen-fixing shrubs include lupine (Lupus species), California lilac (Ceanothus species), and coffeeberry (Rhamnus californica) and false indigo (Chamaecytisus palmensis).

In the herb layer, low-growing herbaceous (non-woody) plants can be found. As a living mulch, this layer helps to keep the soil cool and moist. Think of a mix of annual and perennial veggies, herbs, and flowers that attract beneficial insects, as well as edible and decorative blooms. Most sections of the country lose their herb layer over the winter. Aside from the more well-known Asian greens, comfrey, daylilies, and salad greens in the herb layer, other nitrogen-fixing plants like licorice milk vetch (Astragalus glycyphyllos) can be tried.

Low-growing plants spread out horizontally to form the ground cover layer. Some examples are berries like cranberries, creeping blueberries, kinnikinnick, salal, and wintergreen (Gaultheria shallon) (G. procumbens). Teas and flavorings can be derived from mint, which is also a wonderful source of nectar for honeybees. These plants can cover enormous areas with edible blooms and leaves in milder regions. Clovers are a fantastic ground cover for nitrogen fixers, such as ducks, rabbits, and sheep, that can be mowed or left for grazing.

It includes burdock (Arctium lappa, which is also known as edible burdock and can be obtained in seed catalogs under the Japanese name, gobo) as well as other nutrient searchers, including carrots, dock, and parsnip. Alfalfa, yarrow, and native bunch grasses all have fine, fibrous roots that reach deep into the soil in search of nutrients and moisture. Root-layer plants die over the winter as their leaves decompose and the minerals they accumulate are released back into the soil.

The food forest, like a tropical rainforest, requires climbers who can scale vertical walls. Small spaces can be maximized by using vines to grow on fences, walls, and roofs. Climbing vines can be supported by existing trees in the tree layer, or you can construct your own trellises from bamboo, willow, or other woody plant prunings. Some common examples of annuals that work well in vertical gardens include bean and cucurbit trellises (Nasturtium trellis), cucumber and melons (Cucumis Sativum), pea and squash (Squash Romaine), and tomato (Tomato Plantarum). American groundnut is a cold-season native nitrogen-fixing vine that produces tasty roots (Apios americana). Non-edible nitrogen-fixing vines include Austrian winter pea, sweet pea, and vetch. The one caveat is that some vines are notorious for taking over in certain conditions, so choose wisely (examples include kudzu, morning glory, and trumpet vine). If you're still hesitant, talk to a trusted local expert.

The mushroom or fungal layer is the final one in the food forest. In any forest ecosystem, fungi play a crucial role. Mushrooms need compost or sunshine to develop, and they transform dead organic materials like sawdust and straw into nutritious mushrooms. Never, ever consume mushrooms that you haven't identified, even in a natural forest. To be on the safe side, produce your own oyster and shiitake mushrooms, as well as the tasty but time-consuming 'king' Stropharia mushroom (Stropharia rugoso-annulata), which can be grown in between other crops on hardwood chips, logs, or straw. These are the safest mushrooms to eat.

The permaculture approach known as "stacking," or enhancing a space's yield by combining its components, is demonstrated by putting the food forest levels together. It is David Holmgren's hope that we will stack plants so that we can make the most out of our land and sunlight as well as water. Plants can be stacked in a variety of ways, such as by layering them from the tallest to the smallest. When we plant winter crops under deciduous fruit trees, for example, we know that the naked branches will allow sunlight to reach the herb layer below.

PLANT STACKING

Plants, animals, and structures can all be stacked together. In the "tall tree layer," only the tallest plants grow far above the ground, forming a dense canopy. Our next step is a gradual descent into the soil itself, which is where much of the garden's nutrient-creating job takes place.

CHAPTER 3

THE PERMACULTURE SYSTEM: SOIL FERTILITY

IMPROVING TILTH AND NUTRIENTS

The holistic design method of permaculture makes us think in terms of systems. A system is a collection of various components that work together to accomplish a specific goal and, in theory, form a closed loop. Throughout this section of the book, the many systems that should be incorporated into any permaculture design are discussed in depth. Soil fertility, water quality, energy generation and waste management should all be included in a master plan when it is drawn up. Each of these systems is a significant part of the sustainability puzzle. Keep in mind that permaculture design is a way of looking at things rather than a set of rules to follow as you learn more about these systems in depth. Don't treat the examples as one-size-fits-all solutions that can be applied to every website.

This section includes a number of listings of plants that we consider useful or worthwhile for various purposes. The following details are included in the plant lists, along with any extra notes that may be relevant:

- **Scientific name.** Please familiarize yourself with these plants' scientific names, which will aid in conversation.

- **USDA hardiness zones.** According to the USDA's analysis of average annual minimum temperatures, the United States is divided into thirteen distinct regions. The colder it gets, the lower the number goes in this system. Each plant's hardiness zone range tells you where it is most likely to survive and grow. Whether or not your plant is a success in your location will depend on a variety of other factors, so keep this in mind.

SOIL FERTILITY: IMPROVING TILTH AND NUTRIENTS

A vibrant permaculture landscape is built on the foundation of healthy soil. In order to get the most out of your landscape, it's crucial to keep track of soil nutrients and soil life. And the good news is that no matter how bad your soils are, you can still enhance their tilth and fertility by working with what you have. Once you've assessed your current state, you can begin to think about crops and soil enhancement methods.

ASSESSING WHAT YOU HAVE

Soil testing is a terrific approach to figuring out what's going on in your garden. In order to get a good cross-section of the soil, you should take several samples in the same area and exclude any organic matter that hasn't yet decomposed. Samples can be analyzed individually or as part of a composite sample. The cost of a micronutrient assay should be low, and the results should be comprehensive. Basics like soil pH and the proportion of organic material are included, as well as information on the soil's ability to supply necessary nutrients for plant growth. A reproductive plan that includes supplementing the nutrients you're lacking can be devised as a result.

Soil pH

The pH of your soil informs you a lot about the kinds of crops you can grow and the kinds of amendments you should use. In the absence of a soil test or a pH tester, you may be able to determine the pH of your soil by analyzing the taste or smell of the soil. Acidic soils have a sour flavor and aroma, while alkaline soils have a sweet flavor and aroma. Extreme acidity or alkalinity in the soil can lock up nutrients; hence pH is important. When the pH is between 6.3 to 7.0, the majority of nutrients are readily available. This is the ideal pH range for most plants.

Macronutrients

Plants use a vast amount of nutrients from a variety of sources. Nitrogen, phosphorus, potassium, sulfur, calcium, and magnesium are all examples of these compounds. Plants use nitrogen (N) to grow and produce new leaves. Phosphorous (P) aids in flowering and fruit and seed production in plants. The mineral potassium (K) aids in the development of plants that are more resistant to disease and environmental stress. If you buy a box or bag of fertilizer (organic or chemical), the N-P-K composition is usually listed. Thus, the proportions of the "big three" fertilizers you're providing to your soil may be easily calculated. The nutrient levels revealed in the soil test should be taken into account when using amendments in the soil.

Micronutrients

The nutrients plants require in lower amounts are known as micronutrients or trace elements. Boron, copper, iron, chloride, manganese, molybdenum, and zinc are all essential micronutrients. Even though the actual quantities required are incredibly little, plants will not be able to thrive without them. Look for signs of nutrient insufficiency in your plants using a chart available online. Soil health can be monitored by plants in this way.

Soil life

While it is critical to understand the nonliving components of soil, the living (or biological) components are what aid in the movement of nutrients throughout a soil's structure, all of the measures you use to improve soil fertility can be viewed as ways to provide food for the soil's microorganisms. Some even advocate feeding your soil rather than your crops.

All kinds of organisms are at work in the living component of the soil, such as buffering the soil pH in the root zone of plants, to name just one. Organic stuff is directly decomposed by primary consumers. Fungi, bacteria, earthworms, gophers, and other creatures fall under this category. Mites and other insects, as well as springtails and protozoa, are secondary consumers that feed on the primary ones.

Tertiary consumers are macro-top ecosystem predators. Snakes, lizards, centipedes, and other reptiles are among the food sources for tertiary consumers. To a similar extent that top predators in macro-ecosystems can tell us something about the health of the ecosystem, the existence or absence of these traits in the soil micro-ecosystem can.

Having a wide variety of food sources is the first step in creating a diversified soil food web. Our landscapes will be richer for it. To break down the organic material produced by varied plants, a variety of animals with varying life histories is required.

Soils that are dominated by bacteria are common in ecosystems that are first emerging. Bacteria are particularly well-suited to decomposing nonwoody material, which is why this occurs. Annual gardens and pastures mimic this transitional period in the farmed landscape. In these early successional soils, symbiotic nitrogen-fixing bacteria are an important form of the bacterium. These bacteria are able to transform atmospheric nitrogen into a form that plants can utilize. This parasite can be found on the roots of a wide variety of plants, most notably legumes. Bacteria on plant roots can offer nitrogen to plants and carbon compounds to bacteria.

When ecosystems are in the later stages of their life cycles, they tend to have more woody plant debris that must be decomposed in order for nutrients to flow. Fungi are experts at degrading wood's complicated lignin. To put it another way, soils tend to become more fungus-dominated as ecosystems progress through their life cycles. Fruit orchards and food forests can be found in the farmed environment.

Mycorrhizal fungi are a particularly significant type of fungus. In the same way, rhizobial bacteria form associations with plants; these fungi do the same. Plant roots may be colonized by some types of mycorrhizal fungi, while others develop inside the tissues of the roots themselves. Fortunately, this is a mutually beneficial connection as well. It's like a gigantic network of mycorrhizal fungus spread around the land and connecting it all together. They can aid in the distribution of nutrients and water in the ecosystem. There are fungi that operate as extensions of plant roots, carrying water and nutrients to plants in need. Carbohydrates are exchanged between fungi and plants. Antibiotic compounds are also exuded by some mycorrhizal fungi, which aid in the prevention of plants picking up soil-borne illnesses. Very few mycorrhizal fungi may remain in soils that have been severely disturbed (by scraping or fungicide usage, for example). The mycorrhizal inoculants, which can be used to plant in these barren areas, come in tablet, powder, and gel forms. Make sure you utilize the correct mycorrhizae for the crops you intend to plant.

Your management efforts should be geared to assist the successional condition you are attempting to generate in order to sustain the soil food web. Compost and mulches created from non-woody vegetation and manure should be used in your yearly gardens and pastures to promote the naturally occurring bacteria. If you have an orchard, woodland garden, or wooded area, utilize woody vegetation compost and mulch to help the fungi thrive.

Understanding your soil's physical qualities will help you determine where you need to focus your efforts if you want to bring that soil to a state of production. That's what soil life can do for you. Actually, most soil fertility techniques use the live (or once-living) soil to boost fertility both immediately and long-term. The soil food web management will allow you to produce flourishing, productive landscapes even in the most difficult conditions.

Contaminated soils

Depending on the type of contamination in your soil, it might be anything from petrochemicals to radiation. Pollutants containing heavy metals are common. As an example, the area around an ancient house may be contaminated with lead, which was commonly used as a paint ingredient for many decades. Lead and arsenic, which were used in pesticides for many years in commercial agriculture, can be found in properties that have a history of orcharding, sugarcane production, or other crops. Tacoma's former smelter, which operated for many years, produced hazardous emissions that coated the Puget Sound region of Washington, including the Puyallup area.

Due to the high cost of testing, we only suggest it if there are grounds to suspect contamination. The RCRA-8 test will tell you the concentrations of eight distinct metals in your soil if such is the case. This data can be compared to the average figures in your area to discover if there are any anomalies. Please consult your local extension agency or ecological department if you find it difficult to understand test results.

In the event that pollution is discovered, the following are some options for remediation:

- **Replace the topsoil.** Although it consumes a lot of energy and doesn't truly address the issue (where does the poisonous soil go?), this can be the best choice in some situations.
- **Plant food crops above contaminated soils.** You can always choose to raise your crops above the toxins by using containers, boxed beds, or simply by erecting a barrier between the polluted soil and your imported garden soil. You are less likely to be exposed to the metals through working

the soil or eating the produce if no food crops are truly rooted in the contaminated soil.

- **Add lots of organic material.** You can increase the number of bonding sites available to cling onto heavy metals by boosting the organic content of your soil. Less heavy metals will enter the plants if the organic matter in your soil is able to hold onto it.
- **Avoid root crops and leafy vegetables.** Heavy metals are usually absorbed by plants through their leaves. Even the best washing might not completely remove all heavy metals from roots because they are in direct touch with the soil. It is safer to grow crops away from the ground. The best plants are those whose fruit or seeds you can consume. The fruit and seeds of a plant frequently don't acquire heavy metals from the plant.
- **Use plants or fungi to extract heavy metals from your soils and concentrate them in their tissues, in a process known as phyto-or mycoremediation.** After that, the tissues can be taken from the area and thrown away. You might be able to significantly alter the quantity of contamination at your site over time. The plants or mushrooms utilized in this technique are not suitable for consumption.

FERTILITY MANAGEMENT

As you plan your landscape, fertility management is one of the most crucial considerations. In the absence of internal nutrient recycling, you'll need to rely on external sources of fertility. If you're just getting started with your landscape, this is likely to be the case. To counter this, it is possible to decrease the number of external inputs over time by controlling your nutrients well.

Maintaining an appropriate distribution of nutrients throughout the body is an essential part of fertility management. Nitrogen, for example, can cause plants to grow excessively quickly if it is overused. Disease and cold weather damage can occur more frequently if plants don't have time to harden their cell walls. Nutrient deficiency in food crops may cause a lack of productivity or nutritional value. If you don't have the minerals in your soils, you won't be able to get them in your food. As a result, proper nutrient balancing is essential to both your health and the growth of your plants.

Composting

Food waste, weeds, and brush all contain valuable nutrients that can be released into the soil by composting. Anyone, even those who live in small apartments, can do it. There is a plethora of literature on the subject of composting, but we've compiled a list of various methods for reusing your organic wastes.

Three-bin composting system

Set up three bins that are easy to reach but also rodent-proof with the simple three-bin system. The first bin is reserved for yard debris and kitchen scraps. When the first bin is filled, turn the mound over with a pitchfork and begin filling the second bin once more. When the first is filled again, you move everything down the line and continue filling the first. Ideally, you should have compost ready to use in your garden by the time the first is full again. Due to its piecemeal design, this kind of composting may not always reach hot enough to kill weed seeds.

Worm bins

One of the most useful living species is the worm. The process of breaking down organic matter in the soil's upper layers and converting it into nutrient-dense sustenance for plants is a crucial one. Our worms' excrement can be enriched with bedding and biomass provided for them to digest. With worm composting, the bins are layered on top of each other in a two- or three-bin system. Worm bins, which are more convenient to harvest from, might be as basic as a wooden box or an old Tupperware container. When the temperature drops to 55 to 75 degrees Fahrenheit, it's best to keep your worms indoors throughout the winter months.

A worm bin is nothing more than a box with drainage holes in the bottom. Some damp bedding material is found in this box (Dave likes to use black-and-white junk mail run through a paper shredder). Put some red wiggler worms in the bin and bury some food scraps beneath the bedding at one end of it. Vermicompost, or worm castings, is a wonderful fertilizer for the garden, and they'll do it for you. Adding food scraps and bedding until the bin is full will allow you to harvest your nutrients and begin again. "Worm tea" that drains out of the bottom is a great garden amendment in its own right, thanks to its high concentration of humic acids, which help build up your soil's nutrient-holding ability.

Food waste digester

A food waste digester is an excellent, low-input method for dealing with food waste. Alternatively, you can buy a Green Cone, which you can manufacture at home. There are two parts to the Green Cone: an underground plastic basket and a large plastic cone that extends above the earth. The only thing you need to do is put your food trash into the container at the top. The subterranean basket keeps rats and other pests out while allowing all kinds of soil-dwelling decomposers access to the compost. The Green Cone can be filled to the brim with food waste at any time. It's ideal to have a second one handy, so you can switch to it while the first one finishes cooking. Compost from the first bin can be harvested and used in the garden after the second one is full. It can take a long time to fill if you only put food waste from a small home in there. To put it another way, there will be little to no work needed.

Hot and cold composts

In general, composts that get quite hot during decomposition are called hot composts. Using animal manures and food waste is one way to accomplish this. The majority of the time, hot compost piles are made all at once. As a result of the high temperatures, weed seeds are frequently killed, making hot compost ideal for use in annual beds and regions where direct sowing is required. Because they are more labor-intensive to make and spin and because they lose more nitrogen to the atmosphere during composting, there are various downsides.

In the process of composting, cold composts do not reach high temperatures. Compost piles and brush piles that are gradually replenished are examples of this. Aside from the fact that they require a lot of time to decompose, they are quite low-maintenance. Weed seeds aren't killed as effectively, but the nitrogen they retain is more.

Since they require more maintenance and are more likely to be utilized in yearly gardens, hot compost piles work best in zone 1. They can be placed further out because they may require little to no upkeep and are more commonly utilized near tree crops, but they may also be unattractive. ”

Small animals

A multitude of services can be provided by allowing small animals to forage in the terrain for their own sustenance. Pest management, illness prevention, and fertilization are just a few of the services offered by these companies.

Chickens, sheep, and pigs can browse through your perennial landscape and do less work for you in dispersing the nutrients that they find there. When it comes to keeping his pawpaw (Asimina triloba) patch weed and fertile, Chris Chmiel goes the extra mile. Based on the fact that goats don't like pawpaws, but they'll eat virtually anything else, this technique is simple and elegant. He doesn't have to use nitrogen fertilizer because the animals do it for him.

Animal species can be controlled in a variety of ways to increase fertilization on your property, depending on what you want. Soil fertility can be improved by keeping animals in a contained area, whether by fencing or confined-range systems. Small places like raised beds and lawns can benefit from the use of chicken tractors (a movable floorless pen that can be any form and size).

Soil-building plants

Adaptable pioneer species frequently move in first and improve growing conditions for plants that will eventually take their place if we think about succession from a bare ground perspective. There are several basic features we may seek for and employ to cultivate and maintain our own fruitful soil.

The roots of nitrogen fixers contain a bacterium that can collect nitrogen from the atmosphere and transform it into a form that plants can use. Soil nitrogen deficiency or a need for abundant nitrogen necessitates the search for this trait in plants. Nitrogen-fixing plants include legumes, alders, acacias, and clover. An early successional habitat is ideal for most nitrogen fixers in nature.

In particular, the roots of dynamic accumulators have the ability to mine for nutrients and minerals, which they then store in their tissues. It's well-known that certain plants can store minerals that are useful in a variety of ways. Dandelions, for example, store potassium, phosphorus, calcium, copper, and iron in a dynamic manner. Compost and particular fertilizers can be made from these plants. As nutrient-dense meals or medicine, they can also be consumed by humans.

These companies excel in producing massive amounts of biomass. These plants' leaves can be used to help regenerate organic matter in soils and compost systems, as well as to make green mulch that is simple to apply to landscaping projects. Comfrey, miscanthus, bananas, sugarcane, and bamboo are among the most prolific biomass producers.

Aquatic plants

It's not uncommon for floating aquatic plants, like duckweed, to proliferate at an astonishing rate. Harvest such plants and use them as mulch for your crops to take benefit of this property. This means that ponds can be used even in severely nutrient-poor areas to promote fertility. These aquatic mulches can be harvested and reapplied every few months in warm areas. You may only need to remove this material once or twice a year in chilly climates. There must be enough food for the next generation to repopulate.

Fertigation

Applying water-soluble liquid fertilizers to your crops via irrigation is known as fertigation. It's fantastic since the plants have rapid access to the liquid amendments. Because liquid organic fertilizers tend to clog irrigation systems, fertigation usually requires utilizing a chemical fertilizer solution. This can be done naturally if the correct distribution technique is devised. Aquariums and tanks are excellent sources of nutrient-enriched water. With buckets, sprinklers, or flooding, you can apply this directly to your plants to get the nutrients that you can't get from watering your plants with well or city water.

Biochar

Charcoal is a type of biochar. Burning organic material (such as wood and agricultural waste) in a special stove produces biochar. It's known as pyrolosis, and it's a process that burns the organic stuff except for the carbon under conditions of high heat and low oxygen. After the process is complete, all that is left is biochar, which is pure carbon. Plants can't use it because it lacks nutrients.

Nutrients can bind to it since it has a plethora of bonding sites. Adding biochar to your soil will increase the soil's ability to retain nutrients, even if this does not instantly improve your fertility. In areas with depleted soils, this can have significant implications. It also serves as a habitat for soil bacteria because of its pores.

To get the most out of biochar, it's best to first feed it with nutrients. Soak your newly made biochar, for example, in a mixture of hydrolysate from fish and seaweed extract. In this way, you can use it as fertilizer for your landscaping. If you were to apply these liquid products straight to the soil in some areas, they would probably wash away. In the end, biochar offers a technique to improve soil conditions so that nutrients applied to the soil are not lost but are instead stored for use by plants in the future.

Compost tea

Just like the name suggests, compost tea is made by steeping a mixture of compost and water. There are two types of compost tea: aerobic and anaerobic. Make sure you complete an extensive study before deciding to use this type of nutrient control.

An insignificant amount of nutrients are applied directly to your land when you use aerobic compost tea as a fertilizer. Rather, its goal is to remove and increase the number of beneficial organisms contained in a compost pile and to inoculate your land with these microbes. It's possible that using compost tea can help diversify the soil food web and extend the favorable effects of compost. To prepare aerobic compost tea, you can use a compost tea maker and high-quality compost in a filter bag (homemade or purchased).

As soon as you've filled the brewer with clean water (non-chlorinated or non=chloramined), you'll need to start aerating it using an aquarium pump. Microorganisms will feed on the easily digestible food (flour, fish, seaweed extracts, etc.) that is added at the end of the brewing process. Apply the beneficial tea straight to the soil or to the entire plant.

Fermentation of organic waste can extract nutrients that can then be used on the land with anaerobic teas. If the smell of fermenting food bothers you, this is probably not the method for you. Anaerobic compost tea's effectiveness and potential risks are, in fact, up for debate (such as pathogens like E. coli or salmonella).

Mulch

For healthy landscaping, a layer of mulch should be put on the soil's top layer. Mulch is to blame:

- Protects soil moisture from the drying impacts of sun and wind.
- Spongy organic material in the soil can be used to minimize runoff.
- As a result, the surface of the soil isn't pounded as hard by rain.
- It keeps soil from being eroded and compacted.
- Keeps your plant roots warm in the winter and cool in the summer by insulating the soil surface.
- It can be visually appealing.

Variety is the spice of life when it comes to mulches. Grass, rock, and black plastic are all excellent weed suppressants, but because they don't offer any organic matter to the soil, they aren't always the ideal choice. As a result, we prefer to utilize compost or mulches with a higher percentage of organic content. Weed-controlling dead mulches, like wood chips, compost and rice hulls, need to be reapplied frequently and perform best when spread 2 to 6 inches deep. Clover, vetch, or orchard grass are examples of living mulches. Depending on your objectives and the crops involved, you may need to periodically reduce the number of live mulch crops to allow them to regenerate.

It is possible to reset the biological system by using sheet mulching during the establishment phase. Think about turning your lawn into an annual flower or vegetable garden. Layers of biodegradable material such as cardboard or newspaper can be used to smother the grass, while organic material such as wood chips or compost can be used to weigh it down and replenish the soil. Planting can begin once the foliage has perished and the barrier has largely disintegrated.

Waiting for a shorter period of time and directly planting where the barrier has been perforated is an option in some circumstances. Make sure you inspect the weeds you're trying to cover carefully, as some can grow beneath sheet mulch, such as horsetail and morning glory.

Cover cropping

Protecting your soil and replenishing its nutrients is one of the many benefits of cover cropping. It entails the use of a living mulch that decomposes over time. Crops produced for this purpose are often referred to as "green manures." When crops are harvested in temperate regions, the soil tends to be bare. Soil-building ground covers are best grown in the winter to keep the soil from eroding and to nourish it. Any time you don't have a vegetable crop growing on the land, you can cultivate cover crops in any climate. Recharge soils and interrupt disease and pest cycles. If you're a year-round gardener, finding the time and space to grow cover crops might be a struggle. If you're looking for an edible cover crop, buckwheat and fava beans are both good possibilities, as they do both.

Cover cropping's fundamentals are straightforward:

- Choose and sow your cover crop according to your local climate and requirements.
- The cover crop needs to be properly cared for. Depending on the species chosen, some may need to be mowed or watered, but others may not. Cover crops should require very little attention for the most part.
- Make sure you have a plan in place to get rid of your cover crop before it goes to seed or becomes overgrown. A variety of methods are possible, including cutting the plant and letting the seeds fall to the ground or harvesting the seeds and allowing them to wither on their own.

Rye, legumes, buckwheat, oats, mustards, and sorghum are some of the most common temperate cover crops. Planting the appropriate crop or crops is critical. Depending on the environment and the season, different cover crops might be used at different periods of the year or at different times of the year. For weed control purposes, rye and sorghum are excellent but not so wonderful for seed production because they inhibit the growth and germination of other plants.

With fallowing or resting your land, cover cropping can be used. You can break pest and disease life cycles by planting a cover crop and allowing a portion of your land to sit for one or more seasons.

STARTING POINTS OF SOIL FERTILITY

	Easiest	More involved	Most involved
Recycle yard and kitchen waste	Compost your food scraps	Compost your food scraps. Build a worm bin.	Make your Own biochar.
Use dead or living mulch	Mulch your garden. Collect biomass from neighbors.	Plant green manures (cover crops)	
Use Fertigation or compost tea	Make plant tea to fertilize your garden.	Spray aerated compost tea.	

CHAPTER 4

THE PERMACULTURE SYSTEM: WATER

MAKING THE MOST OF A LIMITED RESOURCE

Despite its importance, water is a finite resource. In our daily lives, it is by far the most crucial natural resource. Drinking water, food production, transportation, and a host of other necessities all rely on water. Fresh water supplies on Earth are dwindling, and as the population continues to rise, they are at risk of being contaminated by chemicals or other poisons and misused. With careful management, rainwater may provide a wealth of benefits and support thriving ecosystems in many areas. In this chapter, we'll learn how to harness the power of this resource for our own benefit.

THINKING LIKE A WATERSHED

Permaculture design relies heavily on an understanding of the hydrologic cycles in your landscape. It's possible to have too much or too little water depending on the weather and the peculiarities of your location. Because water is a valuable and perhaps rare resource, you should recycle and cycle it as much as possible through your landscape.

What questions should you ask yourself about water on your property?

- Where does rain fall and accumulate during a storm?
- Is the hydrology of my location influenced by surrounding bodies of water?
- I don't know how I'm going to get water to drink.
- Where do my toilet and sink water go after I use it?
- In the watershed, what activities are taking place above me that might have an impact on the water I'm drinking?
- How can I use water in such a way that it leaves my property cleaner than when it arrived?
- Where will my actions have an effect below me in the watershed?

HIERARCHY OF WATER USE

Your permaculture design can employ a wide variety of water sources, and you should try to match the water quality to the intended usage. Toilets and gardens in most of our cities and towns use high-quality potable water. Changes can be made, despite the fact that many homes are already wired this way. You might be able to get away with using lower-quality water if you have access to it. Think about the water sources on your property first. Some examples are as follows:

- Rain and snow
- Rivers, streams, and creeks
- Ponds and lakes
- Springs
- Wells
- Runoff from adjoining land
- Municipal tap

The following is a generic list of water uses, sorted by the quality of the water required:

- Drinking and bathing
- Cleaning
- Irrigation and agricultural use (including aquaculture)
- Recreation
- Fire fighting
- Outdoor pond and lake systems
- Infiltration into the ground
- Wetlands

Using this list, you may determine the best use for each of your site's water resources. Water from public taps, for example, can be used only for drinking and bathing. It is not recommended that water from a creek be drunk without first being filtered, but it may be good for irrigation if the water is not polluted. Sediment-laden runoff from a neighbor's fields is not suitable for any of these purposes, but water collecting earthworks may allow it to penetrate into the ground. That water is likely to end up in a wetland once it has been filtered by the soil. Water exiting your property must be as clean or cleaner than water entering your land, thanks to protocols in place.

TAKING ADVANTAGE OF AMBIENT WATER IN THE LANDSCAPE

Water conservation in the landscape is undoubtedly already on the minds of those who live in dry climes. This, on the other hand, holds true for everyone, regardless of location. Because municipal water is more expensive and energy-intensive, we need to do our best to use as much water from the landscape as possible.

Rain barrels and water tanks are popular storage options for many people. Even if that's an excellent strategy for having extra drinking water on hand for specific purposes, in most cases, it will be insufficient. More than 85,000 gallons of rainwater will reach your 10,000-square-foot lot if you live in a dry environment with an average rainfall of 15 inches per year. To make the most of this water, you'll need to employ methods other than simply putting up rain barrels and tanks around your home.

There are a variety of methods for storing water, each with its own set of advantages and disadvantages. It's far easier to take a shower with water from a cistern than it is to dig a well and pull it out of the ground, so keep that in mind when planning how to store water. When it comes to long-term water storage, ponds are frequently the best option. It's important to keep in mind that, even with tanks and ponds, the ground itself is the largest storage reservoir you have.

COMPARISON OF STRATEGIES FOR STORING WATER

TANKS OR CISTERNS	PONDS	SOIL
More expensive per gallon stored		Less expensive per gallon stored
Less permanent		More permanent
Less total rainfall capture		More total rainfall capture
Easier to access for use		Harder to access for use

Priorities for rainwater management

The order of priorities for managing rainwater in the landscape is as follows:

1. Slow the water down to diminish its erosive potential and drop out sediment.
2. Spread the water across the landscape so there is more surface area to absorb it.

3. Sink it into the soil and store what you need for later.

Allowing water to infiltrate our landscape has a number of positive impacts:

- Overland flow and downstream flooding are minimized. Letting the water sink into the landscape slows it down enough that rivers and stormwater systems don't have to deal with it all at once.
- A healthy groundwater resource is maintained, and the aquifer is recharged. The water table can actually be prevented from dropping in dry areas if enough people do it.
- Erosion is prevented. If we slow water, spread it out, and sink it in, we stop the water from flowing forcefully over the surface of the land and eroding it.

Developing the soil sponge

In comparison to something like a slab of concrete, the water holding capacity of a sponge is impressive. Organic matter is what makes our soils absorb water like sponges. It is also essential that you increase the organic content of your soil to improve water infiltration and harvesting.

How much water can soils actually store? Although it varies from place to location and with diverse soil conditions, it is generally more than we assume. Each tenth of an inch of rain can be absorbed by one percentage point of organic material (during a single rain event). With rich topsoil (up to 10% organic material), a natural Iowa prairie may absorb up to 6 inches of rain in a single event; in other words, flooding or overland flow does not occur unless the single rain event exceeds 6 inches in diameter; As a result of the low percentage of organic material in standard Iowa cornfields, floods, erosion, and sedimentation can occur even during rain events of only 1.25 inches.

Keyline design

Keyline design is a ground-breaking approach to water and soil management. Bill Mollison and David Holmgren drew heavily on the permaculture design system pioneered by Australian mining engineer and farmer P. A. Yeomans. The concepts of keyline design can be applied to nearly any terrain, but they work best in large landscapes with undulating hills. Improved water infiltration and a site layout that maximizes water use can be achieved through the use of keyline design principles.

To begin employing keyline concepts in your design, you must first define the slope's primary key point. It's important to note when a hill transitions from one shape to the other, and that's where the key point is. A zone of erosion extends upward from the key point. The movement of soil and organic debris downward is a natural part of any ecosystem. In the vicinity of the critical point, there is a collection zone. The final destination for all of the information from earlier is here. There is a distinct difference between soils above and below the keyline.

On a map, the keyline is a contour line that passes through the key point. To help you plan your landscape, you should know where the keyline is located. In order to prevent soil erosion, you should keep vegetation (ideally forest) on the slope above the keyline. The majority of your producing landscape should be located below the keyline. Farming can continue year after year without damaging the flat ground at the bottom. Orchards and other tree crops can be grown on the steeper slopes below the keyline. For the most part, human settlement may be found along the keyline. High enough to prevent flooding and cold air drainage, yet low enough to avoid steep, eroding slopes and increasing fire danger. Access to the upper, lower, and settled areas of the landscape can be easily gained from a moderately flat road or pathway in the keyline. Keylines are often the highest points in the landscape where huge water storage ponds can be placed safely.

Agricultural landscapes can benefit from the keyline design system's ideas for distributing water. Water tends to flow toward valleys and away from ridges in the natural terrain. Tractor rip lines parallel to your keyline will ultimately start to go off contour because of the difference in landscapes you'll discover on the job site. In contrast to plowing, ripping does not turn the soil but rather creates furrows on its surface of it. It is possible that part of the water that flows downhill toward the valleys will actually drop into the riplines and travel uphill instead. Using this technique, you can effectively disperse water around your property. The greater the spread, the greater the likelihood of an infiltration.

Infiltration and root penetration can be improved over time by ripping lines parallel to the keyline all the way to the subsoil. P. A. Yeomans designed a keyline plow, a specialized ripping instrument, for this purpose. It's difficult or impossible to rip compacted soils, but a 1-inch-deep rip will open up the soil and allow water and roots to penetrate it. Some organic material is likely to be dissolved in the water as it descends. You might be able to dig a little deeper the next year since the soil has become more pliable due to water infiltration and root growth. You'll eventually be able to tear as far as your shank will go. The topsoil will continue to grow over the entire period.

WATER-HARVESTING EARTHWORKS

You can erect earthworks to keep more water on your property in addition to building the soil sponge, which can take years in some cases and applying keyline design principles. Water may be slowed, distributed, and sunk into your environment with a variety of earthworks. These are particularly handy for controlling the amount of water on your site that is either too little or too much.

Installing a curtain drain, for example, can help dry up wet soils in a specific region. Water traveling across the landscape is captured by a curtain drain, which is a ditch built slightly off-contour to direct the water elsewhere. Perforated pipe is often buried at the bottom of the trench, which is then backfilled with gravel. This is useful for moist or spongy foundations.

Installing a dry well is another option for dealing with an overabundance of water. You can dig a hole through the compacted layer of the earth if your site isn't draining properly. A grate can be placed on top of it, or it can be filled with gravel. Drainage into the dry well allows runoff to permeate the compacted layer.

If you live in arid climates with free-draining soils, sinking garden beds into the earth is a great way to maximize your limited water supply. The soil is thoroughly soaked by the water that accumulates in the beds. Raised beds can also help with drainage in damp conditions. In addition to improving drainage, raising garden beds above the rest of the landscape increases the amount of surface area exposed to the sun and wind, which aids in drying.

Infiltration swales and diversion drains, ponds, terraces, and rain gardens are among other earthwork methods.

Drainage swales and swales for water infiltration

Long, meandering basins and infiltration swales are built on contour lines, rendering them dead level. It is the infiltration swale's job to catch rainwater flowing across the land's surface or just below it so that it can slowly seep into the ground over time. If it doesn't reach an impermeable layer, like bedrock, first, this percolation can help to produce a freshwater lens beneath the soil surface. The freshwater lens can be thought of as a big bubble of water suspended above the water table, which the vegetation can use when the water table is low or absent.

In a sloped landscape, adding infiltration swales increases the quantity of water that seeps into the soil and replenishes aquifers. It'll be easier to maintain a healthy water table and less need for irrigation over time. Sediment will be filtered out before it reaches the infiltration swale if bunchgrasses or other dense plants are planted above the swale. To make the most of the soil moisture during dry periods, trees and other crops can be planted on the mound (berm) on the downhill side of the swale (or just below it).

When working on a site with a gentle to moderate slope, infiltration swales are an excellent choice. You should avoid using them on very steep slopes because they are more susceptible to blowouts in the rain. It's possible to make berms out of brush staked out on the contour in certain spots. These will slow down the flow of water and aid in some infiltration, but they won't disturb the soil or gather a lot of rainwater. In addition, all swales should be planned with an overflow strategy in mind. Infiltration swales can either be spread equally across the top of the swales when they are full, or they can be connected to other water-harvesting earthworks via diversion drains.

It is a dip in the ground, but not exactly level, that diverts water from one location to another. In order to move water to a specified spot, they are installed in the landscape off-contour (such as a wetland, a pond, a tank, or a creek). They must have a gentle enough slope to avoid eroding in heavy rains. A reasonable rule of thumb is to have them drop 1 foot for every 200 to 300 feet of distance or more, but if you are unsure, consult with an engineer.

Ponds

A landscape with ponds is not only more visually appealing, but it also serves a practical purpose. The ability to conserve water for irrigation or domestic use, provide a home for wildlife, and provide needed enjoyment in hot climes is a major benefit of wetlands. Ponds can also give opportunities for aquaculture and/or critical fire protection if they are strategically situated in the landscape.

It is important to think about elevation and geography while planning a pond location. Any lower point on the property can be fed by a pond situated high in the environment. Because they don't rely on energy or pumps, gravity-fed water systems are the most reliable. If you're trying to emulate nature, you can create a water storage system that looks like a chain of ponds pouring down a hillside.

Consider the method by which these lakes will be filled, though. Pumping water from a site downstream can also be used to fill ponds if a suitable source is not located high on the slope. When harvesting overland flow, each pond should be larger than the previous one in order to allow a larger volume of water that could be harvested. Large ponds should not be built on steep slopes because of the increased risk of dam blowouts after heavy rains. Before deciding on the size of your ponds, make sure you know how much water they will need to hold (depending on the drainage area's size and the heaviest projected rainfall events).

A few basic guidelines for building a pond are as follows:

- Every pond must have an overflow that goes to a known location.
- Keep woody vegetation away from pond dams, so the roots don't penetrate them.
- In dry climates, try to minimize surface area and shade the water with trees to reduce evaporation.
- When you are constructing a large pond, a complex chain of ponds, or anything that makes you uncomfortable, involve an engineer and/or experienced heavy equipment operator early on.

Soils rich in clay tend to be ideal for ponds. The natural bottom of a clay-lined pond makes it easier to build a thriving ecosystem. Two options exist if your soils do not include clay or do not hold water well (for example, if clay is sitting on top of sand). A synthetic liner composed of EPDM rubber or polyethylene might be used to encase the pond's bottom. There are a few drawbacks to these materials, such as their vulnerability to puncture by animals or people and their tendency to become slippery due to algae development, but overall, they are excellent at holding water.

Terraforming will be necessary regardless of the method used to encapsulate the pond in order to build flat benches at varying depths.

This will not only allow for a larger variety of plants and animals to thrive, but it will also make it easier for swimmers to get out of the water. Potted water plants like water lilies, lotuses, and wapato can be displayed on flat benches in liner ponds.

Terraces

Terraces may be an option if you lack flat terrain for access roads, structures, human areas, or crops. Terraces restrict the flow of surface water, preventing erosion, and they also serve as infiltration swales, allowing some water to gently seep into the soil.

It is very easy to create tiny terraces, but terracing big landscapes can be a labor-intensive undertaking. In addition, terracing can cause serious harm to the surrounding land if done incorrectly; therefore, it's important to consult an expert before undertaking this type of earthwork.

Without retaining walls, terraces can be constructed. There may be no need to build a wall with a slope of less than 25%. Retaining walls should be used if the slope is between 25 and 45 percent. In order to keep the terrace in place on a slope of more than 45 percent, it is recommended that dense vegetation be planted as well as consulting an engineer.

Rain gardens

In a rain garden, a shallow dip in the landscape is used to collect water from neighboring impervious surfaces. A swale-like depression allows rainwater to slowly seep into the ground. An organic and mineral-rich Bioretention soil mix is used to fill it. According to the region's climate, rain gardens may be swamped by significant amounts of rain or dry for an extended period at a time. These architectural components are commonly seen near parking lots, parking strips, and tiny yards, where water from impervious surfaces is channeled to them by design. They reduce the amount of water entering municipal stormwater systems in metropolitan areas. Instead, it is utilized to replenish the groundwater table and reduce the amount of irrigation required. Determine how much space you'll need for stormwater storage in a rain garden by measuring the collection surface and comparing it to the soil percolation rates.

MANAGING WETLANDS

Your options and duties expand dramatically if the land you're dealing with contains any type of marsh. Our planet's wetlands produce the most biomass of any landform. They act like the earth's kidneys, filtering and purifying the water that flows through. Wetlands, on the other hand, can be harmed by human activity. Many countries have imposed severe regulations on what people may and cannot do in wetlands, which is understandable. Wetland restrictions, on the other hand, rarely allow for the incorporation of productive usage that does not inflict any harm (or, in some cases, actually restores wetlands). As a result, some of the ideas in this section may not be legal in your area.

When working with wetlands, we must follow the precautionary principle: Don't do harm. If the intended activity in your wetland degrades or reduces the biological function of the area, you should reconsider your strategy. Wetland health can be gauged by a number of factors, including:

- A healthy population of amphibians
- A diverse population of macro-invertebrates
- Good water quality as measured with a simple lab test
- Lack of silt and sedimentation eroding from the nearby landscape

Restoring the ecological function of a wetland that has already been harmed should be your top concern if you own the land. Sediment and pollutant sources can be identified and addressed. Wetland edge vegetation can be beneficial in both circumstances. Soil runoff from surrounding agricultural areas can be captured by vegetation, and plants that absorb nutrients can be used to prevent excessive nutrient imports. It is possible to grow plants that are beneficial to both humans and wildlife in these strips of vegetation. You can reestablish ecological function by reintroducing native plants, animals, and macro-invertebrates once pollutants and sediments have been cleaned up.

If you're prepared to put the health of the wetland first, there are ways to increase the productivity of wetland areas. Chinampa agriculture, modified crops, and the lo'i and paddy systems are only a few examples.

Adapted crops

Many crops may thrive in wetland environments. Most of these plants can tolerate seasonal or persistent flooding, or they can be entirely submerged. Choose crops adapted to wetland conditions, and your wetland regions may be produced without major alterations if you choose these types of crops.

Chinampa agriculture

Aztecs in Mexico's lowlands developed Chinampa agriculture by altering wetlands to produce agricultural opportunities. These people would stack brush in shallow marshes in order to generate a dense matrix of woody debris. Once this rich, fertile marsh muck was dug up and piled on top of the brush stack, canals were dug around it, raising the ground level by roughly a foot. In order to keep their newly formed "island" together, the residents would plant wetland tree species along the perimeter. Mesoamericans were able to produce enormous quantities of food on these "chinampas," as they were known since water flowed up from the swamp. When it was time for harvest, canoe access to the chinampas made it easier to transport produce to the major cities.

Chinampa farming on a small scale is still possible today. In wetlands, creating small chinampa peninsulas and islands can help species that prefer year-round access to water. Trees like hawthorn and Hawthorne are good fruiting plants for these climates. The willow can be used for basketry, wattle-and-daub building, and other crafts.

Lo'i and paddy systems

Crop cultivation was common in many Asian and South Pacific tribes, with some even going to consider measures to build their own wetlands. Polynesians, for example, used the lo'I method to build terraces that cascaded down valleys. As the silt and water accumulated on these terraces, ideal growing conditions for wetland taro were created. Gravity would carry water from one terrace to the next. Both erosion and flooding were also taken care of by these methods.

Think of the Hawaiian lo'i system, where fish and plants grow in terraces, one on top of the other. Fertilizing the plant terraces with fish poop and cleaning the fish poop with fish manure would be a win-win situation. A series of plant terraces at the end of a lo'i system will help ensure that any water that is recycled back into the ecosystem will be free of contaminants.

Rice paddies have been kept on slopes for thousands of years in nations like Japan and China. Much wildlife has adapted to the paddy conditions through time and now relies on the human farming system to suit their needs. The integration of industrial systems and ecosystems is possible thanks to these systems.

RAINWATER CATCHMENT AND STORAGE SYSTEMS

Rainwater is a priceless resource if you have the necessary infrastructure in place. When it rains in urban and suburban regions, rainwater is drained away as quickly as it falls. A rainwater collection and storage system is an essential component of any permaculture design in order to prevent the waste of this valuable natural resource.

When considering the design of such systems, keep in mind that they are made up of a variety of components.

- Sources: Where does your water come from?
- Collection: Where is the water in question being collected from—a roof, driveway, city street, spring box?
- Distribution: Once the water is collected, how is it transported through the system—pipes, hoses, trenches, pumps?
- Storage: After collection, where is the water stored—barrels, tanks, ponds, cisterns?
- Overflow: When any given storage method in the system reaches capacity, where does the excess water go?
- Points of use: Where is the stored water used—sinks, spigots?
- Cleanup: How is the spent water cleaned after use?
- Recycling or returning to earth: How does the water get looped back into another part of your system or returned to the earth?

If you're planning a rainwater harvesting water system, you need to think about all of these components. The system will not function if any component is missing.

Collecting potable water from a roof

For potable use, it's critical to consider the roofing type, how to deflect the first flush, and filtering while collecting rain from a roof. The only definite way to know if the water you're drinking is safe is to do a water test.

- **Roofing material.** Because of their propensity to emit toxins throughout the course of their lifespan, asphalt shingles are a poor choice for rainwater harvesting. Roofs made of metal are among the most sanitary. Galvanized metal, on the other hand, can potentially leach pollutants into the water as it passes over it, making painted or sealed metals the ideal option. Insofar as they're not treated with moss killers or other herbicides, natural materials like thatch and wood can be a viable option for roofing. Using slate or clay tile to catch rainwater is a terrific idea.

- **First, flush diverter.** Surfaces where your water is gathered accumulate debris such as leaves, bird droppings, dust, and more. To prevent that first flush of rainwater from clogging your pipes, you'll need to install an additional device known as a "first flush diverter." Commercially accessible products, as well as simple do-it-yourself options, are both available for this straightforward gadget for roof and gutter systems. You can make first flush diverters out of a spare pipe that is slanted like a T before the water drains. Clean water can flow over the ping-pong ball and into the main collection unit because the chamber is sealed with a float and filled with dirty water.

- **Filtration.** Filtration is critical if you plan to use the water for drinking or cooking. Options for making water safe for consumption include ceramic filtration, reverse osmosis, and ultraviolet radiation. As long as you design it carefully, you can create your own low-tech biological water filter, the slow sand filter.

Slow sand filters can be as small as a 5-gallon bucket or as large as an entire community's worth of sand filters. The more water a system can process in a given amount of time, the more efficient it is. The incoming water is filtered by a layer of microorganisms that grows on the sand's surface. Sand layers filter the water as it descends. Upon reaching the bottom of the filter, it can be emptied into the outflow tube and sent on its way in pristine condition. The outflow pipe must be lower than the intake. The biological agents that could damage you should be rendered harmless to a great extent by this basic system. Specialists can also be hired to help you find out how to filter large groups of people or more complicated systems.

Storage options

Depending on your requirements, you can store water in a variety of methods, including barrels, tanks, cisterns, and ponds. Materials and dimensions vary widely among these items. Storage unit choices can be hampered by a lack of available space or a tight budget.

Remember that very few individual ever complain about having too much water storage capacity while you're deciding how much storage space you need. In order to determine the best system size for your needs, consider the following:

- How much water can you possibly catch? You can figure it out by using this simple equation: (average annual rainfall in inches ÷ 12) × (square feet of collection area × 7.48) = gallons per year. For instance, if you lived somewhere with 50 inches of rain per year and you had a roof of 100 square feet, you could catch up to 3,100 gallons of rain in an average year.
- How much water do you use? In order to figure this out, you'll need to estimate, and you may want to split potable water use from irrigation.
- What is the longest period you are likely to go without rain? In other words, what is the longest period you need to get by without your rainwater tanks getting recharged?
- What are your goals? Do you want to completely disconnect from municipal water? Do you just want to use rainwater to flush your toilet?

Here are some storage options:

- Plastic storage tanks are common and easy to find in a variety of sizes and colors. It is important to choose dark colors to keep out light and prevent algae growth.
- Metal cisterns are often cylindrical and more expensive but last longer and can be more attractive than plastics.

- Ferrocement, which is a mixture of Portland cement plastered over the woven metal mesh, is a great material for larger systems but can be more labor intensive to build.
- Slim cisterns are becoming more popular in urban areas where space is limited. They can be much more expensive than agricultural storage units but can double as a privacy screen or wall in many cases.

The water you collect can be stored in a variety of ways, including infiltration tactics and mulching, as well as in the built environment.

Rain barrel systems

Resilience can be enhanced by storing as much water as feasible, regardless of your site's water budget. For the sake of efficiency, it is best to start there; it is also a less expensive and less complicated water system. As a starting point, we recommend a rain barrel system that may be expanded upon.

The rain gutter's downspout flows into a new garbage can that has a coarse filter on top to catch any stray particles. Despite the fact that it should be simple to clean, a window screen is frequently used to cover the aperture of this coarse filter. Additional storage is provided by plumbing two garbage cans together. Water must be able to fill both tanks simultaneously; therefore, make sure that the connection between them is completely watertight and as low as the containers will allow. To increase your storage capacity, you can chain together as many cans as you wish. On one or both tanks, the spigot should be located low on the tank. A pump and further filtering are required to use the water from these tanks for anything other than irrigation. Nevertheless, in an emergency, the water can be disinfected.

The outflow pressure is increased by placing the garbage cans on a platform, which increases the gravitational pull. A man-made structure like a pallet or a block can also be used to raise the garbage cans, but keep in mind the weight of water once they're filled. One tank's overflow is positioned at the top. If you don't have a plan for where the overflow water will go, you'll have nowhere to put it. A rain garden or infiltration swale may be used, or the overflow may return to the existing stormwater management system if one is already in place.

Integrated gravity-feed water systems

The most efficient and resilient water system design is the fully integrated gravity-feed system, which is a step up from the rain barrel system. A system like this employs gravity to carry water to where it's needed when all of its components are at the correct height. A water harvesting system like this one is ideal for capturing potable water and then using the excess to benefit the community. Water can be taken from a variety of sources and sorted into tanks for different purposes with this technique. If gravity is a concern, some of the system's components may not need to be housed in the same location. You can use the water from a taller building in the landscape to supply a lower building.

A coarse filter and a different type of the first flush are used in this type of starting system. Afterward, the non-potable water is put into the first tank. This tank's water can be used for a variety of purposes, including irrigation and infiltration. A slow sand filter is used to remove any impurities from the water before it can be used for drinking. It is possible to use greywater from a hand sink that is fed by a potable water storage tank in the landscape. Storage components must have an overflow plan that is lower in elevation than the inflow of the next component in order to prevent overflow.

You can increase your storage capacity by adding additional tanks and connecting them together. As long as the two tanks are connected at their apex, the second one can serve as an overflow reservoir while the first one is left unattended. Water levels will remain constant if they are joined at the bottom, essentially creating a single tank. An old-fashioned jack pump can be used to draw water from higher elevations than the storage containers, and it doesn't require the usage of electricity to do so.

A low-tech pump is used to pump water into a water tower in a complete water system (preferably run on renewable energy such as solar). The jack pump isn't necessary because a water tower can supply enough pressure for a gravity-feed system (although it can still be a good backup). If your point of use is higher than your storage, or if you wish to boost water pressure, a water tower is a need. In the event of a power outage, if you already have water stored in a tower, that volume will flow to your point of consumption via gravity. Adding another tank to the system allows for more storage space for secondary purposes.

WATER CONSERVATION

Freshwater conservation and protection are becoming increasingly vital in our global society. One billion people on the planet suffer from water scarcity, according to WHO estimates. Droughts may become more frequent in some locations as the climate becomes more unstable. In many urban locations, the water supply systems are overworked. In some places, the year-round climate is one of extreme aridity. Even in the face of uncertainty, it's always a good idea to save water in the landscape. From the simplest (behavior change) to the most difficult (technological solutions), the table outlines strategies to save water (building new systems).

WATER CONSERVATION WAYS

	Changing behavior	Upgrading what you have	Building new systems
Bathroom	Change your flushing habits: if it's yellow, let it mellow; if it's brown, flush it down. Take shorter showers. While brushing your teeth, be sure the water is turned off.	Get a dual-flush toilet. Use high-efficiency showerheads.	Compost all human waste (no water needed). Add a pedal sink.
Washing dishes and laundry	Hand washes using as little water as possible.	Use high-efficiency machines.	Add a pedal-powered washing machine.
Irrigation	Use plants with water needs that match your climate.	Use drip irrigation.	Install a greywater system along with earthworks to capture runoff.

CHAPTER 5

THE PERMACULTURE SYSTEM: WASTE

PLUGGING LEAKS IN THE SYSTEM

A near-zero-waste system is what you want to aim for in your permaculture design. That doesn't have to happen right away, but it should be a top priority for the organization nonetheless. Your systems will always need enormous amounts of external input if you build them to be wasteful. This is how most lawns look. Without the use of chemical fertilizers, city water, and gasoline to power the lawnmower, they would swiftly deteriorate.

Nonrenewable external resources comprise a large portion of our daily use (at least in a human timescale). They're gone as soon as we use them. Because we rely so largely on these resources for day-to-day operations, we are more vulnerable to market and supply chain volatility and thus less resilient. What happens if we are forced to rely on outside sources for all of our basic needs, such as food, water, and heat?

Leaks are common in systems, and this chapter explains how to eliminate them, thus reducing waste. To put it another way, we're trying to find a means to recycle such "surpluses" (another term for "waste" taken in a different light). It's possible to avoid throwing away food if we make compost, for example. We don't waste energy if we follow the principles of effective energy planning and the next highest usage. Our systems' incoming and outgoing data must be kept under control. A closed-loop system (one in which nothing enters or leaves) isn't in the cards for the foreseeable future, but it's a goal worth striving for in the interim. In the end, we want to pay close attention to how our systems' outputs can be used as inputs. No matter how much water we use, it shouldn't have any negative consequences for the environment or our neighbors.

The trash from people, greywater, food and yard waste, and even heat should be taken into consideration while creating your design. In the previous chapter on soil fertility, we discussed different methods for converting food and yard waste into compost. In this section, we'll examine the other topics.

HUMAN WASTE

Humanure, or the management of human excrement, is considered taboo in Western society. Bringing it up in polite conversation is out of the question. However, we must begin to take responsibility for the humanure we make. Although many of us have come to depend on centralized systems and typical house septic systems, they don't fare well on their ecological report cards. Sewage from cities and towns around the world is often thrown in the ocean or injected into the groundwater. Even municipal systems that are more environmentally friendly require a lot of power. There is no way to estimate how much water is wasted as a result of these technologies. If you think about it, large desert metropolises like Las Vegas and Phoenix have so many flush toilets that the Colorado River no longer makes it to the Gulf of Mexico.

If you don't want to contaminate water or burden others by flushing your human waste, there are a slew of creative options available. There are ways to incorporate this outflow back into your permaculture design that is neither gross nor unhygienic. In order to take responsibility for your own humanure, you must ensure that it is handled in an environmentally safe manner.

When it comes to toilet removal, it is imperative that you thoroughly educate yourself on the subject. Laws and regulations differ from one region to the next. Regardless of your decision, you should at least be aware of their existence. Temperature and timing can vary from one situation to the next. Start modest and do a lot of study before trying any of these methods at home. Also, bear in mind that attention to detail is a prerequisite for any humanure system. Each of these systems requires careful attention to the precise temperature, timing and cleanliness requirements. Even if that doesn't describe you, flushing it will likely be better for everyone.

Flushing your toilet with greywater is an interim measure that can assist limit negative effects in the meantime. Greywater can even be pumped back into the toilet tank using a toilet lid sink. There are two critical variables to consider while choosing a humanure management system: water table and culture. You'll need to consider your location and the depth of the water table when deciding which choice is best for you. Using an outhouse where you drill a hole in the ground, fill it with human excrement, then cover it and move on in a place with a high water table is not recommended (as an aging septic system might also do in this case).

You can avoid dealing with human waste by using this method if your water table is high enough to leave behind large, spongy plugs of composted material that can be accessed by the plants around it. When deciding on a humanure management system, you need also consider the local culture. For example, in a global setting, there are some countries where people use toilet paper and other places where people clean themselves with water. This will have an impact on your decision-making process. A family farm or campground has a very different culture than an office building in the middle of a city. In one context, it is acceptable to transport sawdust and human waste in wheelbarrows, but not in another.

Consider your audience and how receptive they are to new ideas before writing anything. A new user will also need to learn how to prevent messing up the system (nobody wants to deal with poop in a urine excluder). Context is critical for all of the permaculture methods we advocate. For both users and administrators, a well-chosen system may save waste and improve the overall experience.

Waterless composting toilets, constructed wetlands, and biodigesters are some of the best ways to deal with human waste.

Waterless composting toilet systems

Water conservation is best served by waterless choices. Each time you make a deposit, you must add some carbonaceous material like sawdust or wood chips to keep the carbon-to-nitrogen ratio in check and keep the odors and flies under control in these systems (just like a cat burying its poop in kitty litter). The addition of some red wiggler worms can also help. The worms will avoid the hot center of the pile and remain close to the exterior, assisting in the movement of waste materials inside the pile to ensure more even composting results. Devices known as "urinary excluders" can also be used to keep urine out of these systems. This prevents the urine from mixing with the humanure and causing unpleasant odors, as urine is the source of the most offensive odors.

Clivus Multrum and Sun-Mar are only two of the many prefabricated composting toilets on the market. Such systems are permitted by building codes in several parts of the country. A two-chambered composting toilet is an ideal design if you wish to build your own. A concrete, ferrocement, or stone vault supports the throne. As a result, the vault is separated into two sections, each with a large ground-level entry port. When one side is filled, switch to the other side and finish your business. The first side should be mostly decomposed by the time the second side is full. In order to finish composting, you can remove the material from the compost pile, turn it, and place it in a specified spot (protected from both animals and rain). There's no trouble developing a three- or four-chambered system for a larger gathering of individuals.

With a chimney, the fumes can be disbursed at a height where people aren't likely to be present. In order to prevent fumes from rising back up through the throne, install a sheet metal covering that extends lower than the vent pipe. It's actually possible to feel the air being drawn down the hole and subsequently released by convection, leading to a stench-free throne experience if this is done correctly.

In addition to the two-chambered method, a bucket system can also be used to eliminate the use of water. A toilet seat connected to the top of a 5-gallon bucket is all you need. Once a week or so, you empty the bucket into a designated humanure composting area, where you can add your carbonaceous material. Composting can take several months, with occasional turning. The advantage of this system is that it does not necessitate large construction, but it does necessitate a more extensive administration of the infrastructure.

Composting toilet feces: What do you do with it? To ensure that pathogens are killed in the compost, you must research the temperature and timing of your environment and conditions. Solarizing the humanure under glass may even be a good idea. If a pathogen manages to persist, you should avoid applying humanure on crops that may come into close contact with your food (for example, root vegetables, lettuces, asparagus). Mulching trees, ornamentals, and other non-edible crops using humanure is an excellent option.

Flush options

A flushable system may be more suited than a waterless one in some situations. Blackwater is the term used to describe the sewage that is ejected from a toilet. All of these methods wastewater, but by finding a means to make use of the waste, the amount of water that is wasted can be dramatically decreased.

Engineering wetlands is a fantastic approach to using biological resources to manage blackwater. In a word, when you flush, the wastewater flows into an aboveground network of wetland "cells" that you've constructed. Blackwater travels through these cells, much like in a septic system, and microorganisms break down the organic material. Nonwoody wetland and prairie plants can be used instead of woody ones in a septic system to help absorb nutrients. Engineered wetland water tends to be cleaner than municipal wastewater treatment systems in most cases; however, this is not always the case. Although this water should be checked regularly, you may use it to water your garden. Obviously, these systems are expensive, but the expense can be divided among neighbors because a single system can handle numerous residences.

Other options include biodigesters, which are tanks that collect and digest the waste from flush toilets and produce biogas. This process produces biogas. Methane is released and captured throughout this procedure. Fuel can be generated from this methane. Composting the digestate, the leftover material from the biodigester, yields a pathogen-free fertilizer that may be used on crops. Both animal manures and organic waste can be digested via anaerobic digestion. Biodigestion is a municipal waste management method in Lloydminster, Alberta, Canada, where garbage is collected and converted into energy and other products.

Many household cleaning solutions, such as bleach, contain toxins that kill the microorganisms responsible for processing the waste, so be cautious if you use one of these systems to handle your blackwater. For toilet cleaning, hydrogen peroxide, vinegar, and baking soda are the finest nontoxic choices.

Pee cycling

Urine is an intriguing by-product of the human body. In most cases, it exits the body free of infections unless the person is ill. If we mix it with our human waste or blackwater, we may end up wasting a valuable resource. Nitrogen is found in large amounts in human urine. Plants can readily use the nitrogen in urine because it is in a form that they can readily use. As a result, one of the best nitrogen fertilizers you can use in your garden is your own urine. According to a study from the University of Kuopio in Finland, one person's pee can develop more than 150 cabbages per year. Consider separating the management of urine and humanure from a design standpoint.

Using urine in the garden poses a very low danger of spreading pathogens. If you have a medical condition or reside in an area with extreme temperatures, you should do more research. As a general rule, salmonella kills after a few hours of being expelled from the body. You may want to delay harvesting urine-fertilized crops for a few days following your final treatment to prevent the risk of salmonella contamination. Six months of fermentation before use is also an option. This will make it smell, so there is a trade-off involved. If you're collecting other people's urine, you might want to think about this.

When you're ready to use your pee, you have a few options:

- In locations with good drainage, you can apply it directly to your garden. You can dilute eight parts of urine with eight parts of ice-cold water. Make sure to distribute the salts evenly if you're using your fresh pee every day. In addition, this will help to prevent unpleasant odors.
- Compost piles can benefit from the addition of urine to assist expedite the decomposition process. Use a carbon-rich compost mix to tolerate the additional nitrogen if you do this.
- Greywater irrigation systems can use urine as a source of irrigation.

GREYWATER

Greywater is water that has not been tainted by human waste before it is used. Dishwashers, laundry washers, kitchen and bathroom sinks, and showers are all included in this. It is possible to reduce the amount of pure tap water needed to irrigate a productive landscape by using greywater instead of it.

After scrubbing vegetables or washing clothing, greywater can be put to good use in the landscape. There are two unbreakable rules for any greywater system:

- **No surface greywater.** Greywater can be put to the soil surface, but it should not be left there for long periods of time. It's time to reassess your system's design if it includes any pools, puddles, aqueducts, or greywater ponds. Septic systems may develop in any of these, and animals of all kinds may become vectors if they come into contact with greywater.
- **No greywater storage.** Your greywater will become septic if it is stored in a large tank until you are ready to utilize it; Smell and potentially dangerous germs may result. Avoid systems that store greywater for longer than 24 hours. Furthermore, greywater should be handled like blackwater.

Those who plan to reuse greywater must avoid using household cleaning products that contain chemicals that can leach into the water. Two grey water systems that operate exceptionally well are dishpans connected to the yard and branched drain systems connected to mulch basins.

Taking a dishpan out to the yard is as easy as it appears. You can use a dishpan to wash your dishes and then dispose of the water at the base of a tree. Greywater can be collected in a bucket and emptied every day if you remove the bathroom sink's P-trap. Make sure to seal the sewer pipe if you do this to prevent gas from returning to your home.) If your soil percolates, then the water you pour on top should be absorbed within a few minutes at most. This system's low implementation costs are a major selling point.

The ultimate in greywater systems is a branched drainage system for mulch basins. An Oasis Design plumbing element known as a flow splitter is made by Art Ludwig, better known as the Greywater Guru. The water entering the flow splitter is split into two if it is located at a dead level in the landscape. Four pipes, each carrying a quarter of the total load, are created with three flow splitters.

A basin dug into the ground in an area with good drainage, sufficient distance from the water table, and surrounding perennials that you wish to irrigate should be the final destination for each of these irrigation lines. The depth of the basin should be around 16 in (actual size will vary depending on your percolation rate and volume of greywater produced). It is recommended that you use a mulch to line each of these urns. Pick coarse wood chips or similar materials that won't float easily. Each mulch basin should get one-quarter of the total volume of greywater that travels through the system. To avoid breaking our first guideline, it will immediately fall below the mulch. Bacteria in the mulch basin clean the greywater in this system. Plants in the area will benefit from the nutrient leakage, as will the water itself.

It's possible to employ infiltration technology to transition between pipelines and mulch basins, but it's preferable to just let the greywater light up for a few seconds before it sinks in. When the mulch starts to degrade, it may be necessary to remove it and replace it. Mulching other neighboring trees with the material that was removed is a great use for it.

Special considerations for the winter months may be required in countries with extremely cold climates. It is feasible to begin the process by putting in a valve that allows for a choice between sending greywater to a branching drain system and sending it to the traditional sewage system. In the event that you need to reroute the water in the winter or for any other reason, you can do it easily.

FOOD AND YARD WASTE

Many methods of recycling food and yard waste have previously been discussed in the earlier chapter on soil fertility. Just one more wonderful approach to repurpose woody debris from pruning, plant removals, and other regular gardening jobs will be mentioned below. Hügelkultur, which roughly translates as mound culture in German, is a process of layering organic material and covering it with soil to form a bed for crops. A variety of scales can benefit from this technique.

Simply layering organic material of various coarseness, starting with logs and twigs, and then layering finer material on top, is all that is required to build a hügelkultur bed. Topsoil is the final layer, followed by a finer layer of organic matter such as manure or compost. Mulching with wood chips or straw is an option if you prefer to plant directly into the soil. The organic material inside the mound progressively decomposes, providing the plants with water and nutrients.

HEAT

Heat is a waste product that is often disregarded. The majority of biological processes create heat. A burning process necessitates the use of heat. Heat is generated by the sun. If you live somewhere where heat is scarce for part or all of the year, you should consider strategies to collect heat that is attempting to escape your systems as a matter of urgency. Greenhouses, hotbeds, and even housing designs that position human living quarters over animal stalls can trap the heat created by animals and compost piles (remember that heat rises). To avoid losing heat, you should only take cold showers to prevent this from happening. Using drain line heat exchangers, you may recover some of the heat and reuse it in your hot water heater. It is important to think beyond the box and recognize heat in a resource.

SALVAGE

There are numerous ways in which we can benefit from other people's system vulnerabilities. If you live in the developed world, it's easy to get your hands on materials that can improve your land's fertility and functionality. This type of garbage is very prevalent in urban settings. Check to check whether you can use something that already exists before you buy new ones. Apples can be traded for wood chips from your local arborist, for example. Garden mulch can also come from neighbors who don't use pesticides to keep their grass healthy.

Although we want to take advantage of these resources, we must be careful not to become overly reliant on them. It's possible that many of these "waste materials" will become sought-after commodities if permaculture design takes off (and we believe it will). That 5-gallon bucket of coffee grounds from your neighborhood coffee shop that you pick up every week may have some competition. Imagining a day when it becomes too expensive to carry goods around the world is a scary thought. Think about what would happen if the waste products you depend on dried up because the procedures that produced them were impossible or unprofitable. Remember the transitional ethic, as well. Make use of these wastes to strengthen your future resilience, but don't get dependent on them for day-to-day needs. When it comes to soil fertility, this implies not relying on foreign sources but rather generating the fertility your land requires on-site (or locally). Energy, water, food, and shelter are all affected by this.

CHAPTER 6

THE PERMACULTURE SYSTEM: ENERGY

MINIMIZING THE WORK WE DO OURSELVES

The ability to perform tasks is referred to as energy. There is a lot of work to be done in our permaculture systems. Using nature's patterns as inspiration, we can construct systems that require few external inputs, produce minimum pollution, and operate at a high level of efficiency. Systems that reuse and recycle energy are our ultimate goal. It's our goal to do as little as possible ourselves. Think of a system in which your orchard is not only fertilized by sheep but also cleaned up by them.

Most of us think of electricity when we hear the word "energy," yet for many of us, that phrase actually refers to fossil fuels. Using energy in permaculture design is more than just generating electricity. There are many other ways energy can manifest itself, and electricity is only one of many possible guises. This chapter will focus primarily on electrical systems, although we'll begin by focusing on other methods of generating energy, which typically leads to more elegant and less-technical designs.

Be careful to include your energy systems as part of your overall strategy. Starting small and making progress is the best way to learn about your entire energy picture and reduce the negative effects on your life at the same time. As your knowledge grows, you will be able to accomplish more.

NONELECTRIC ENERGY

The most energy-efficient systems don't even require any electricity. Even electricity produced by renewable energy systems such as solar panels has an efficiency cost attached to it. Heat or light is lost energy changes form anytime, according to thermodynamics' second law. Because of the two conversions, using photovoltaics to convert sunlight into energy and then using that electricity to heat water results in an efficiency of less than 15%. Before the hot water can be produced, the photovoltaic panel loses 85 percent of the solar energy that it receives. In many cases, the most efficient method of accomplishing a task is to do it directly from the source (for example, heating water with the sun's rays). If you use a flat plate collector to heat the water directly, the efficiency of the energy conversion can exceed 75 percent, resulting in only a 25 percent loss of solar energy.

You should look at non-electric methods of accomplishing tasks first, given that electricity isn't the most efficient way to get things done and requires a considerable lot of technological know-how to generate your own. Let's take a fresh look at the idea of acceptable technology. What is it about technology that makes it acceptable? Depending on the technology and the person asking the inquiry, the response will be different. What are some of the most frequently asked questions?

- Is it clear to you how it all works?
- If it breaks, can you fix it with local materials?
- Is there a person in your neighborhood who can accomplish these things?

It's possible that the technology in issue isn't the best fit for you or your situation if the response is no. Non-electrical methods exist for capturing energy, either passively or aggressively (with moving parts). In reality, everything from grinding grain to lighting dwellings had to be done without electricity prior to the Industrial Revolution. In this way, history and current innovation combine to provide us with a wide range of good passive and active energy solutions. Anywhere in nature where there is movement, there are inventive methods to make that movement useful for doing tasks.

Active systems

One sort of movement can be transformed into another using an active system. Compressed air and pedal power are just a few examples of alternative energy sources. Waterwheels. The power of moving water can be converted into a spinning shaft with the help of a waterwheel. Reciprocating saws and lathes can be powered by a rotating shaft with the right gearing. Grain mills and water pumps have both traditionally been powered by waterwheels.

Windmills

Similar to a waterwheel, a windmill can be used to harness the power of flowing air in windy regions. Grain milling and well water pumping are two common applications for this sort of equipment.

Pedal-powered devices

They have been around for a long time and are one of the most efficient machines ever made. It's a great approach to harnessing the power of biological energy for small- to medium-sized projects. Pedal-powered blenders, grain grinders, oil presses, water pumps, and nut shellers are all available.

Water-powered pumps

Mechanical pumping solutions are available if you have flowing water on your land and need to transport some of it uphill. Pumps powered by running water move a tiny volume of water uphill in a pipe using the energy of the water's flow. Each pump of the piston moves only a little amount of water, but these hydraulic pumps operate continually and can move a significant amount of water without the need for energy.

Compressed air technology

It is possible to store energy without using electricity using compressed air (or pneumatic) technology. Pneumatic wrenches are commonly used to remove or replace your car's lug nuts in an auto repair shop, and the sound you hear is similar to that of a pneumatic wrench. Pneumatic tools are also employed in dentistry, demonstrating the versatility of pneumatic instruments for fine detail work. It is possible to compress air using a wide range of mechanical and electrical technologies. Compressed air can be used to power a wide range of shop equipment, as well as transportation vehicles.

Passive systems

This means less friction and less wear on passive systems because they don't have any moving parts. Mechanical failures are highly unlikely in these systems due to their extreme robustness. Solar water heaters and dehydrators are among them.

Solar dehydrators

Preserving foods using processes such as fermentation, freezing, salting and canning has been practiced for thousands of years. Another option to extending the life of your crop is to dehydrate fruits, vegetables, and herbs. To some extent, this depends on where you live and how much solar power you currently have available to you.

Making your own solar dehydrator is as simple as following these steps:

1. You should start by finding a slope with the best possible solar orientation. On the slope, the dehydrator has to be placed so that the solar panel is lower than the dehydrator unit itself.

2. Remove all but the shell of an old refrigerator and discard the rest. If you're unsure about how to safely remove the refrigerant, get the assistance of a professional. Most places prohibit the discharge of greenhouse gases like freon into the atmosphere.

3. In order to attach a metal tube from the solar panel, cut a hole large enough in the bottom.

4. A stovepipe can be attached to the top by making a hole big enough (6 to 8 feet long). Make the connection between the stovepipe and the union watertight.

5. To prevent rain from dripping down the chimney, paint the outside of the refrigerator and stovepipe black and put a cover on top.

6. In the refrigerator, install a rack system for screen trays.

7. You can make the collection panel by painting a piece of roof metal black, then mounting it in an opaque box (the longer, the better). Only the holes at the bottom and the top of the box should be open so that hot air can flow from the panel into the refrigerator, and cooled air may flow out of the panel. Protect the bottom of the collection panel from animals and insects by using wire mesh and/or a screen.

8. Connect the collection panel's top to the refrigerator's bottom hole with flexible metal tubing in an airtight manner.

A rise in temperature will occur when sunlight hits a collection panel. During its ascent, the stovepipe will expel air, and additional air will be taken in through the openings at the base. To put it another way, your product will continue to dry as long as the sun shines on it. Your food should be ready in one to four days, depending on the type of drying you're doing and the amount of sunshine you're getting.

Solar hot water

The use of solar water heating has been around for some time, but it is becoming more common. Solar hot water technology is one of the renewable energy infrastructure solutions that offer the fastest return on investment. Prefabricated evacuated tube or flat panel solar collectors are the most common, although you can create your own if you want to. Passively heating water in your hot water tank with the sun's rays is the goal of these collectors. A solar hot water system can at least heat the water a portion of the way, which means less energy, propane, or natural gas is required to bring the water to a temperature suitable for home usage. Using antifreeze in the panel and a heat exchanger in your water tank, these systems can be employed in cold climates. A thermosiphon allows water to circulate through the system without the use of pumps when the collecting panel is positioned lower than the storage tank.

Natural convection is used in a thermosiphon to passively circulate fluids. It's based on the physics of rising heat. A thermosiphon can be used in a solar hot water system by placing the storage tank above the heat collection panel because hot water naturally rises. A storage tank above is the sole option for it. The water cooling down in the storage tank, on the other hand, rises to the top of the heat collection panel, where it is recirculated back to the storage tank. The absence of mechanical pumps makes thermosiphon-based systems more robust by design.

Biological systems

There are numerous methods by which biological systems can be used to generate electrical power. Human biological energy is harnessed through pedal-powered systems. Animals and flora are other potential resources (for biofuels).

Animals

Animals' physical products, such as food, fiber, and fertilizer, are often the first things that come to mind when we think of incorporating them into our permaculture gardens. Many animals also provide us with a source of energy that we can put to good use in our daily activities. Horses, water buffaloes, and oxen can all be used for field traction. People have relied on horses, camels, and oxen for thousands of years to transport themselves and their products. In addition to producing heat, all warm-blooded animals do so as well. Even domesticated animals like dogs and cats have a long history of doing tasks for human benefit. Most dog breeds were created for a specific reason, as a matter of fact. Make sure you think about how your dogs can help you out.

Biofuels

In most permaculture plans, there is room for small-scale biofuel production as well. Using wood in a wood stove, for example, is an example of a biofuel. This is a better option than using fossil fuels or nuclear power if you want to keep your house warm. However, burning emits carbon dioxide into the atmosphere, which is a contributing factor to global warming. As a result, if we want to cook meals and heat our homes effectively, we need to look for low-pollution stoves. Methane produced by biodigesters can be utilized in cooking, as well as for heating and cooling.

Perennial oil and sugar crops should also be included in your landscape if you want to be able to produce at least some of the oils and sugars you use. Larger landscapes and homesteads can benefit from edible oils from African oil palms, walnuts, and coconuts, which can also be turned into biodiesel for use in diesel engines or utilized directly in diesel engines that have undergone the required conversion. As a result, the oils you generate can be used to power equipment like generators, automobiles, and even some hand tools. There are also culinary goods that come from the cultivation of sugar crops, including sugarcane, sugar beets, and sorghum. As a beverage, a preservative for herbal remedies, or an alternative fuel for modified gasoline engines, they can also be fermented into alcohol.

ELECTRIC ENERGY

Electricity is a vital part of the modern world. In reality, writing this book required a lot of electricity. Using electricity often means consuming nonrenewable resources (such as fossil fuels) or generating radioactive waste (in the case of nuclear power plants). As long as we don't take care of this important resource and think about our impact on other people and ecosystems, we'll likely be supporting systems that hurt them. If we're going to practice permaculture, we've got to take responsibility for our own electrical production as well as consumption.

Designing for sustainable energy production and consumption in permaculture is a primary goal. Electricity is the most complex and time-consuming to comprehend of all the energy sources we've examined thus far. Despite this, it is the most advanced energy source we will likely ever have access to, and as a result, it has an almost limitless number of applications. To put it another way, even if the process of producing electricity is complicated, it is incredibly simple to transform that energy into a variety of useful types of labor.

It is suggested that if work can be done directly using the sun, wind, or moving water without the additional step of creating electricity, you should think about ways to make that happen. You should only use electricity when absolutely necessary (such as computers, stereo equipment, and televisions). Heat is a low-grade energy source. It has a restricted range of uses but is quite simple to create (you're currently manufacturing some). Your design should be less wasteful and more efficient if you are relying on the use of energy to generate heat.

Performing an energy audit and reducing your consumption

In order to construct a renewable energy system, the first step is to measure and reduce your energy consumption. By doing this initially, you may be able to reduce the size of your renewable energy system.

Real money and non-renewable resources can be generated from these savings. Existing structures can benefit from an energy audit. An energy audit can be done on your own if you have the time, or you can hire a professional. Energy audits may be eligible for financial incentives in some municipalities, states, and utilities. You'll be able to see where inefficiencies exist, as well as how to remedy them, after doing an energy audit. It makes it logical to start with the simplest and most inexpensive options, such as switching to more efficient light bulbs and adding weather-stripping.

The amount of electricity used by your various appliances and devices can be measured with an energy-monitoring device called Kill A Watt. This could be eye-opening for some people. See how the power demand changes when you vary the level of your audio when connected to *Kill A Watt*.

Even after you turn off your devices, you may find that they continue to use electricity. Phantom loads refer to these kinds of demands. It's a smart initial step to identify and eliminate them by unplugging gadgets when they are not in use or plugging them into power strips that can be turned off.

ENERGY CONSERVATION MEANS

	Changing behavior	**Upgrading what you have**	**Building new systems**
Heating and cooling	Wear a sweatshirt and decrease the thermostat a few degrees. Take a swim when it's hot.	Improve weather stripping and insulation. Install a programmable thermostat. Build trellis or shade houses to keep cool.	Install a home power system to supply electrical needs.
Lighting	Turn off lights when not in use.	Install solar tubes for passive lighting. Use low-wattage task lights when possible.	
Electronics and appliances	Turn devices off when not in use. When the weather is nice, hang your clothes to dry instead of using a dryer.	Find and eliminate phantom loads, so energy is not used when devices are off.	

Considerations in designing a home power system

Designing a home power system is all about making the most of the resources you have available and maximizing the amount of energy you can generate. In your site A+A, you should have indicated the energy resources that are available to you. Is there a steady wind at your location? Is the location well-suited to capturing energy from the sun? What kind of water source is available on the site year-round? Does the availability of any of these resources (streams dry up, winds seasonal, and winters are cloudy) fluctuate at different times of the year? It's crucial to remember that hybrid systems can be used to boost resilience and meet power needs all year round because most regions have seasonal variations. It's a good idea to combine solar electricity with wind power, for example, since in the winter when there's a little sun the winds speed up, and in summer when they're quiet, it's much sunnier.

You should build your power system to make the most of the energy you do manage to harness, in addition to having many inputs. The batteries of solar-powered off-grid systems in sunny climes may be fully charged by 10 a.m. The rest of the day's solar panel energy will be wasted unless a mechanism is put in place that prioritizes the electricity harvested in order of priority. For example, recharging batteries is a major concern. Once that's done, the shop's compressed air tank can be refilled with additional power. Water could be pumped to a high-altitude tank or pond if the batteries and compressed air tanks are full. Water features, fans, aerators, and other non-essential, non-time-sensitive technologies could all benefit from the remaining electricity.

Some of the more advanced techniques for storing extra energy include hydrogen fuel cells, flywheels, and spring compression. When you think about all the things that need to be done in your home, look for ways to get more power to do them.

When putting in electricity systems, start small but prepare for expansion. Many people start off with a very basic system and work their way up from there. It's better than destroying eight or twelve batteries because they only lose one or two. It's possible to build a power system that can grow toward your final aim if you know what you want it to look like in advance.

There are some components that are worth oversizing from the outset. A little oversizing of the charge controller and inverter, for example, can allow you to add more solar panels to your system and grow it over time without having to buy completely new equipment. The old hardware can also be exchanged or utilized somewhere else as an upgrade path. Prior to beginning any project, take a moment to think about the consequences of your actions.

Grid-tied and off-grid systems

When developing a renewable energy system, one of the most important decisions is whether or not to connect to the current grid infrastructure. With the grid, you don't need any batteries because the grid functions as your "battery" for your system. On the other hand, if you use more electricity than your system produces, you'll have to pay for it. It is feasible to sell excess electricity back into the grid at a wholesale rate in some areas. Power is lost when the grid is disrupted, which could be at a moment when you need it most. If you don't have a battery backup or a gas-powered generator, you'll miss out on a lot of the benefits of having your own power system.

An off-grid system's key benefit and drawback is the use of batteries. It is possible to store power in a variety of ways with batteries, each with its own set of advantages and disadvantages. Batteries made of deep-cycle lead acid are the most often used. A good quality lead-acid battery can survive ten to fifteen years or more if it is properly cared for. It's not uncommon for folks to occasionally drain their batteries to the point of irreparable damage. Despite being recyclable, lead-acid batteries are the system's Achilles' heel. Nickel-iron batteries, which can last three to four times longer and do not leave behind an exceedingly poisonous heavy metal at the end of their useful life, may be a superior (albeit substantially more expensive) alternative. As a result, off-grid systems necessitate a higher level of maintenance and energy management on your part.

The fundamentals of a home's power system

The components of most renewable energy systems can be summarized as follows:

- **Collector.** Photovoltaic panels, wind turbines, micro-hydro systems and generators are the most prevalent collectors. If you're mechanically minded and open to experimenting, you may want to look into pyrolysis machines and tidal power, which are less prevalent and more experimental.
- **Batteries.** This is where you keep the generated electricity.
- **Charge controller.** The brains of the system are in this key piece of hardware. Using this, the system is able to direct the flow of electricity. It protects batteries from being overcharged, which could lead to damage or safety concerns.
- **AC inverter.** Direct current, or DC, is the most common type of electricity generated by your system. Most of our appliances and electronic devices, on the other hand, are wired to receive alternating current (AC). It is, therefore, necessary to use an inverter unless you acquire DC appliances and equipment exclusively. Do your homework, evaluate your requirements, and then decide whether to go with an AC system or a DC system, or even both. In addition, make sure you're familiar with your appliances and equipment. Laser printers and delicate stereo equipment, for example, may require extra electricity. Laptop computers and other electronic devices can run more efficiently on a DC system with a DC adapter than on an AC system with a conventional AC power supply.
- **Fuses, breakers, and shutoff switch.** It's critical to have the ability to turn off the electricity entering the system in the event of a malfunction. The usage of circuit breakers and fuses should facilitate this. Switches allow you to turn it off at your own convenience. For varying levels of protection, these can be positioned in various parts of the system.

- **AC or DC loads.** These are the electrical devices you're utilizing, whether they're powered by AC or DC.

COMPARISON OF AC AND DC POWER

AC	DC
Best for long wire runs (>100 feet)	More suited to short wire runs (<100 feet)
Generally, 120 or 240 volts = higher risk of electrocution	Usually, 48 volts or lower = minimal risk of electrocution
Works with almost all common appliances and equipment	Works only with DC appliances and equipment, which can be more difficult to find and/or expensive
Requires an inverter = expense	Does not require an inverter = savings of money and energy
Generally easy to create a system that meets code	Challenging to create a larger system that meets code
Many inefficient or wasteful appliances available	Many high-efficiency appliances are available
Possible health risks from long-term exposure	No suspected health risks

REMEMBER: You begin with patterns and work your way down to the tiniest details when building your energy systems. Everything else should fall into place without too much difficulty once you've made sound fundamental judgments.

CHAPTER 7

THE PERMACULTURE SYSTEM: SHELTER

BUILDING FUNCTIONAL, EFFICIENT STRUCTURES

A great deal of consideration goes into the design of our permaculture structures and how they are integrated into them. Structures have the potential to save a lot of energy and resources because of how energy- and material-intensive they are. Your structures must make sense in the context in which they are used. A good place to start is by looking at how traditional and indigenous people build (or built) their homes. Designing structures that are both efficient and pleasant to live in requires a thorough understanding of local materials, energy sources, and climate trends.

THE IMPORTANCE OF CLIMATE APPROPRIATENESS

For a structure to be useful prior to the Industrial Revolution, it had to be located and constructed in a manner that was sensitive to the climate. Buildings that were suited to the climate were more likely to endure and be passed down through generations. Because of this, people were able to build dwellings that were more comfortable in scorching deserts, airier in humid tropics, and at least somewhat warm in freezing climes.

During the Industrial Revolution, fossil fuels became widely available at a low cost. To put it another way, it meant that inefficient buildings might be made habitable simply by slamming a lot of resources into the problem. Even today, we're still following this tendency. We tend to design structures that satisfy our aesthetic preferences while overlooking climate appropriateness, site conditions such as aspect and orientation, or the availability of local resources in the process. Fossil fuel-powered heating and cooling systems are commonplace in many parts of the world. A lack of fuel inputs would lead to a number of these structures becoming untenable, if not completely uninhabitable, for at least some portion of the year.

This type of architecture, which relies primarily on traditional, local techniques and resources, may teach us a lot. As a result of a lack of access to energy, indigenous and traditional peoples in an area's building traditions have evolved to avoid wasting resources due to shoddy design decisions. The ultimate in climate responsiveness, their techniques and material choices evolved over time as a result of their environment and cultural context. The majority of traditional peoples lived within their present solar income and worked with what was available in their immediate area. As permaculture designers, that's exactly what we're aiming for.

This raises the question: How can we design buildings that are more efficient in terms of upfront and long-term resource use while still serving their intended purpose? " This subject necessitates a thorough examination of three facets of structural design: site selection and basic layout, building materials, and methods for controlling temperature.

SITING AND BASIC DESIGN

A detailed examination of the natural forces at work on the site is essential to the success of a building's design and location. Even if you don't want to compromise the building's performance, it's crucial to take advantage of outstanding views (or hide unsightly ones). As a result, when planning and building a structure, you need to take into account aspects like sun, wind, and fire hazards. If the house burns down, is stifling hot, or forces you to consume a lot of fuel to keep warm, the view won't be of many services to you. Keep in mind our principle of relative position as well. What is the relationship between your building and the other structures on the property? Just think about it: where do you get your energy? Creating gravity-fed water systems is hampered or facilitated depending on where your building is located. How easy is it to get to your building from where it is located? Buildings are often long-lasting structures. Try out a few different positions before making a final decision. Type I errors, such as those caused by inefficient construction siting, can bog down a project for years. Sun, wind, and fire can all have an impact on a building's position.

Sun and passive solar design

One of the most important considerations when planning new structures is the sun's position. When it's freezing outside, the sun can help keep your house warm, or it might make it unbearably hot. The interaction you want between your building and the sun should take your local climate and the site's aspect into account. Homes built on south-facing slopes benefit from the sun's warmth and illumination in the temperate Northern Hemisphere. While this is true in the Northern Hemisphere, the polar opposite is true in the Southern Hemisphere. You may want to avoid the sun in equatorial climates. There is little difference between north and south on the equator compared to east and west since the sun's path doesn't alter significantly over the course of the year. On the other hand, sunlight in the late afternoon is significantly more intense than that in the early hours of the day.

Your building's orientation in relation to the sun should also be determined by the type of structure you are creating. A fruit cellar, on the other hand, needs to be kept cool and out of the sun in order to preserve its produce. Including components in a building's design that operate in concert with the sun to boost the efficiency of the structure passively is known as passive solar design (with no moving parts). As with any excellent permaculture design, a passive solar design must have a solid balance of several aspects. On a sunny day, even in the dead of winter, a room with no mass can become unbearably hot from the sun's rays.

Orientation

The first step in increasing the effectiveness of passive solar construction is to change its direction. Buildings should be positioned such that their widest side is facing the sun (south in the temperate North, north in the temperate South). In the winter, windows can be placed on the sunny side to maximize solar gain. Heat loss can be minimized by reducing the number of windows on the house's shady side and increasing the amount of insulation in these walls. Light can enter a building through clerestory windows, reducing the requirement for active lighting equipment. Clerestory windows can do a great job of letting hot air out in the summer if you can open them.

Shade trees, eaves, and trellis

So that only low-angle winter sun heats your home's interior while keeping out high-angle summer sun, you can avoid overheating your home by installing appropriately sized eaves on its sunny side. Trellises on the sunny side of the building can also help achieve this appearance. With deciduous vines like grapes or kiwis covering the trellis, you can shield your plants from the sun during the sweltering summer and early fall months but still let some light in during the winter and early spring when you need it most. You may get the same effect with the correct shade tree species—trees that shed light, dappled shade rather than deep, black pools.

Masonry floors and thermal masses

In the winter, dark-colored stone floors complement the warmth provided by south-facing windows. Heat is absorbed by the floor and then radiated back out when the sun goes down, when it passes through the windows and hits the dark stonework. Trombe walls, cob seats, and half brick walls inside the windows can all help with thermal absorption. As a result, fewer active heating systems are required.

The use of specific colors on purpose. In addition to passive solar benefits, the colors you choose can also help. Light hues reflect heat, while dark colors absorb it. By painting south-facing walls with a light tint, you can help keep buildings cool during the hot months. Choose light wall colors inside the structure to generate brighter places with more surfaces to reflect ambient light. It is possible to save energy by using fewer electric lights or candles.

Solar tubes

While reducing the number of windows on the house's shady side helps keep heat in, it also reduces the amount of light coming in. With the inclusion of solar tubes, this can be addressed for both exterior and interior spaces. Solar tubes in the roof bring natural light into these shadowy areas, reducing the need for additional lighting. It is possible to improve building efficiency to the point that no active heating or cooling systems are required in some regions by combining all of these strategies. Even if you do require those systems in your climate, you'll probably be less dependent on them. In addition, the atmosphere in these settings is fantastic to be in. The increased amount of natural light and the more comfortable surroundings have a calming effect on the human mind.

Wind and windbreaks

As with sunshine, the effects of wind on your structures can be either positive or bad, depending on the situation. Wind can have a significant impact on the amount of energy required to heat a home in a cold temperate environment. The opposite is true in the lowland tropics, where you want as much airflow as possible to keep cool and minimize mold growth.

Many of the negative effects of windbreaks can be mitigated if your structures must be located in a windswept area. In addition to lowering heating expenses, windbreaks can:

- Make it more pleasant to be outdoors,
- Protect crops from wind damage,
- Create wildlife habitat,
- Block pesticide drift and blowing dust,
- Prevent plants from desiccating, and
- Prevent weight loss in livestock.

For temperate areas, windbreaks can provide additional benefits by allowing snow to fall on the lee side, resulting in greater drifts that melt in the spring and supply water for your land. To either replenish your local aquifer or provide adequate moisture for tree crops during the growing season, this infiltration is an option.

Designing an effective windbreak

You need a well-designed windbreak to get these advantages. Long-term, a single row of trees can act as a windbreak, but this is a dangerous strategy. What would happen if one of those trees succumbed to the effects of aging? A hole will be left in the windbreak as a result. The Venturi effect causes the wind passing through that opening to accelerate. As a result, the nearby trees and whatever lies on the other side will suffer. As a result of the additional stress on the nearby trees, they may also perish. A single row of trees could easily turn out to be an expensive blunder.

Think about how windy some shorelines may get and notice that, in general, the flora grows in size rather than forming a tall, vertical barrier. As a result, wind turbulence is minimized on the other side of the windbreak.

The tallest pieces of a windbreak determine how much space they shield. As a general rule, a windbreak provides inadequate protection for a distance up to ten times the height of the tallest point in its vicinity. After it has matured, a windbreak made up of 60-foot-tall fir trees can shield an area from the wind that extends 120 to 300 feet in all directions. A set of windbreaks can be used to drive the wind back up before it touches down again if you need to protect a bigger area than one windbreak allows. Shelterbelts are a common name for such systems. Shelterbelts once spanned a large portion of the Midwest. Agricultural practices that encourage the "fence line to fence line" planting of commodity crops have resulted in the loss of many of these species over time. This is a true pity, as the shelterbelt forests (which were fairly large) offered timber, wildlife habitat, and ecological benefits, as well as protecting row crops like corn and wheat in the interim. Investigate the possibility of using shelterbelts as part of your design if you're working with an open, somewhat level area.

A windbreak works best if you don't try to completely block the wind. It is best to have a windbreak that is anywhere between 40 and 50 percent permeable. Damaged turbulence will ensue if this is not the case. When planning your windbreak, it's best to incorporate both evergreen and deciduous trees and shrubs that can withstand wind. Adding greater permeability can be accomplished by cutting some of the trees, but avoid removing lower limbs, as this defeats the function of the windbreak and allows it to be torn apart by the wind beneath the surface.

Leaving a gap in a windbreak can have the same effect as a missing tree in a single-row windbreak, which is why it is often required to give driveway access. Instead, create a zigzag path via windbreaks so that you can enter one area and exit another.

Windbreaks are actually microclimates that we construct. Sunshades are an excellent illustration of this concept being put into practice. As soon as Bullock's Permaculture Homestead was purchased, it was covered with young fir and madrone trees on a south-facing hill. First, permaculture practitioners cut down some of the young trees to create a scalloped pattern in the forest, like a fish scale pattern. When they built homes and gardens in one of these scallops, they also planted fruit trees in others. All three sides of these scallops were shielded against cold winds coming in from all directions. The glossy leaves of the adjacent madrones also reflect sunlight into the open area. Much more dark-colored granite has been exposed to the sun in the cleared regions. All of this adds up, and the microclimates created by these sunshades warm up sooner in the spring in order to help with output.

Building a temporary windbreak

When the wind is so powerful that young trees are blown to the ground, how can you build a windbreak? Temporary windbreaks are the answer. Your windbreak should succeed if you allow the species you've picked to establish their roots before the wind blows them over, as long as they're well-anchored and wind-tolerant.

To begin, consider what you may use to create a temporary windbreak. Old hay bales and brush piles are excellent options. You could even scavenge through the trash left behind by previous occupants. Use the old Buick you found in the woods to plant that oak tree before you scrap it.) It is also possible to use buildings as windbreaks for anything that is coming downwind of them. Planting in pits is an option if drainage is good. The windward side of the pit could benefit from a mound made from the pit's dirt.

A Filipino fence is another type of temporary windbreak. This structure is especially useful in areas where working and establishing plants are hampered by a persistent driving wind (or anything else). To build a Filipino fence, begin by sinking some posts into the earth in a line that is nearly perpendicular to the direction of the wind. For a natural look, thread some kind of flora through the 6-inch square concrete reinforcing wire that is attached to the posts (or lash it on). Palm fronds, small-diameter bamboo, reeds, and grasses are some of our favorites. Your windbreak is now ready to serve you for several weeks to a year.

A fast-growing vine, such as passion fruit (Passiflora spp.), can be planted at the foot of each post at this time. The vine fills the area as the vegetative screen deteriorates and falls apart. In time, the vine will cover the entire fence, and the vegetation will fall to the fence's base, where it will be used as mulch.

Using a Filipino fence, you can construct an arc form that encourages the wind to travel around the outside and over the top. You may shield your nursery stock from the wind by keeping it close to the fence on the lee side. It's also possible to set up a tent camp with an outdoor kitchen and composting toilet, as well as an indoor bathroom and shower. The first layers of your windbreak should be planted on the side of the Filipino fence that is facing the wind.

Fire

If you live in an area where fire used to play a significant role in the natural ecology, you'll want to take special caution when deciding where to site your structures and what to put between them and potential fire hazards. Fires are more likely to break out in areas with a lot of dry weather in the summer. You should avoid building your home on top of a hilltop in these climates, as fires can spread swiftly uphill.

MATERIALS

Most buildings' primary role is to shelter us or something else. However, there are several more requirements that are so obvious that we don't even think about them. Using modern building materials, we frequently run into this issue.

Our first priority is to ensure that our buildings do not pose a risk to our health. Many typical building materials contain elements that are detrimental to the human body. Off-gassing from new materials, such as carpets and finishes, is a common cause of poor indoor air quality. A condition known as "sick building syndrome" has even been documented in which people grow ill after spending time in a structure that has been constructed using harmful materials.

As a second goal, we want to avoid utilizing building materials that harm the environment in any way. As an example, the production of polyvinyl chloride (PVC), a material extensively used for pipes, window frames and flooring, as well as its disposal, has significant environmental implications. When goods are shipped from other countries, their embodied energy is high. Local materials that produce minimum environmental impact during their life course are the best choice for both of these challenges.

When it comes to building materials, we don't have to look far back in time. Our goal now is to combine the greatest modern building materials with the best local, natural materials that have been used for thousands of years.

Balancing local and natural with sensible

When deciding on building materials, keep in mind that there is a trade-off between local, natural, and practical. An outstanding result is achieved if you can select building materials that match all three of these criteria. In some cases, one of these may be elusive, expensive, or impossible to obtain.

For example, if you live in an area where good clay and straw are readily available, cob could be a great building material for you to use. That being said, your city may not allow you to use it. That might lead to a long and costly battle with your local government. It's also possible that earthquake resistance necessitates the usage of materials sourced from beyond the area. Despite the fact that few of us have local supplies for cement and steel, we may still need to use them in our buildings.

Do your best and pay attention to the materials you employ in your building. Before putting any item to use, do some research on it.

Thinking about thermal mass and insulation

It's important to select the right materials for your building project based on your requirements. Using a thermal mass instead of an insulative material will not produce the desired results. The usage of thermal mass in dwellings helps to reduce temperature swings. Assume you have a large black rock in your garden on a beautiful day. That rock gets a lot of heat from the sun all day long. It reflects heat back into its surroundings after sunset, helping to keep the space around it a little cozier. Thermal mass can be achieved by using natural materials like cob, adobe, and stone.

Heat cannot pass through a good insulating material (or cold). To keep your body heat within the jacket rather than leaving through the open spaces of the fluffy down, you need a down jacket. In contrast, Styrofoam coolers insulate because of the air space in the material, which prevents the liquids inside from warming up. As insulators, natural building materials such as straw and old denim can be found in many homes.

The R-value (R for resistance) is a measure of how well a particular material resists the flow of heat in construction. Insulation value increases with increasing number.

Some common natural construction materials have the following R-values:

- Straw bales: 1.45 per inch
- Straw-clay: 0.9–1.8 per inch
- Wood chip-clay: 1.0–2.0 per inch
- Granite: 0.05 per inch
- Brick: 0.2 per inch
- Blown cellulose: 3.8 per inch
- Wood: 1.0 per inch
- Wool: 3.5–3.8 per inch

Choosing natural materials

Biomass and dirt or stone are the most common base materials used in natural architecture. Biological and earth or stone materials include wood, straw, sod, and bamboo, as well as earth (adobe and cob), clay (bricks and ceramics), stone, lime, and sand; Cob, straw bales, wood, stone, wattle and daub, straw clay, and wood-chip clay are just a few of the natural building techniques you can use with these resources.

Cob

When sand, clay, and straw are mixed together to form a cob, they form a solid wall that can stand alone (not corncobs). Making individual cobs, which are balls of the elements blended together in uniformity, is the beginning. These are smoothed together after being stacked and layered. It is possible to build about a foot of cob a day so that it has time to dry and strengthen. If your soils are clay-rich, you may be able to use cob and earth plasters. (To determine your soil type, perform the shaker jar test outlined previously in the book.) Make an earth oven in your backyard and use it for baking your own pizzas for a terrific first cob-like project. It is not necessary to mix the cob elements in an earth oven since they utilize clay-sand on the interior, then light clay straw for insulation, then chop straw and earth plaster for the finish.).

Straw bale

It is possible to build walls out of straw bales that are extremely insulating. Plaster is then applied to the interior and exterior of the walls. For moisture resistance, natural earth plaster is frequently used with a lime plaster finish. When utilized as a wall filler, straw bales can also be used to support the weight. Straw bale walls make excellent workshop and studio partitions if you're just getting started. Practice on these buildings before building a house out of these components. Practice in an environment where you don't have as much to lose.

Wood

Pole construction, timber framing, and post and beam construction all rely on wood as a primary building element, which can be found in abundance almost anywhere trees grow. It's a terrific technique to use wood without cutting it first to build structural elements out of entire branches and small trunks, or "round wood." This results in a reduction in consumption. For the same cross-section, wood in the round has more inherent strength. If you're interested in learning how to perform woodworking, a good place to start is with simple projects like trellises and sheds. It is possible to apply the concepts you learn from building simple structures to more complex constructions.

Stone

Using masonry skills and fine stone may produce some of the world's most long-lasting structures. Stone, on the other hand, has little insulating value and is best suited for applications where strength or bulk is required. Foundations, sheds, retaining walls, and other outside infrastructure should all be considered.

Wattle and daub

Using thin diameter trees (typically coppiced) or bamboo, the wattle and daub technique weaves a wall like a basket. The daub, a type of earthen plaster, is used to cover the wattles. Non-load-bearing walls can benefit from this technique. If you're just getting started, a simple room divider made of wattle and daub can be a good place to start.

Straw clay and wood-chip clay

Filling the area between posts with a mixture of straw or wood chips and clay creates an insulative wall. To begin, build a trough between the poles using boards (just like forms for pouring concrete). In the event that you're working with straw, you can cut it into smaller pieces. Afterward, you spread out the straw or wood chips and pour a thin layer of clay slip on top of them. Mix it all together and use a stick to press it firmly into place between the form boards. The straw should remain in its original location after removing the forms, allowing you to begin working on the following layer without having to move the forms down. This method is quite efficient. In order to retain the straw or wood chips where they are, you can cover them with earth plaster. Retrofitting houses with poor wall insulation can benefit from this. Adding insulation is as simple as tacking a frame to the outside of an existing, inadequately insulated wall.

HEATING, COOLING, AND TEMPERATURE MODERATION

Keeping buildings comfortable in both hot and cold weather is an essential aspect of a comprehensive energy-saving strategy. In what ways can we create structures that use the least amount of energy to maintain a comfortable interior temperature? How can we use the least amount of energy and produce the least amount of pollution when we do require additional heating or cooling?

Heating

As a goal, your house should be heated entirely by passive solar architecture and not require any additional heat. However, in other cases, this may be a tall request. A woodstove is one of the most straightforward ways to heat a room. For those who live in distant, cold-winter regions, having a backup plan can be of essential importance. Wood is a readily available and environmentally friendly fuel in many regions of the world. To ensure a stove that is both efficient and environmentally friendly is to do some study before purchasing it. Keep in mind that even though wood may be replenished, its combustion contributes to climate change. If you have alternatives that don't necessitate burning anything, go for them first.

With a chimney that goes through a big thermal mass, the firebox of a Masonry stove or Rocket Mass Heater is combined with a massive firebox. You'll be able to store and use more of the heat your fuel produces this way. Burning a fire once a day can provide enough heat to keep a house warm for an entire day.

Heating technology relies heavily on distributing heat throughout a facility in order to meet demand. Radiators were used to distribute heat in old-fashioned boiler systems, which piped steam throughout the structure and radiated it. Hydronics is a popular modern method for accomplishing this. Heat can be distributed throughout a building by running polyethylene tubing heated by a stove or other method through the floors and walls of a structure. A thermal mass, such as an earthen floor, can be used to store and release large amounts of heat throughout the course of the day and night. It makes sense to insulate beneath an earthen floor with Hydronics in order to prevent heat from escaping into the earth and instead reradiating into the living space.

The usage of an attached greenhouse or solarium in areas with sunny winters can help conserve heat. The interior of a building is heated by sunlight entering via windows (a perfect illustration of the greenhouse effect). During the day, open the doors and vents to let warm air enter the greenhouse and close them at night to keep the greenhouse from overheating.

Designing a single structure that serves several purposes while conserving space and resources is possible when you consider creative ways to generate and recycle heat. When the hens in the illustrated garden structure use their inside run, it helps keep the greenhouse warm in the winter. Chickens need a place to lay their eggs and a place to get out of the hot sun, and the chicken coop provides both. The greenhouse's heat loss is minimized thanks to the toolshed's dark, insulating backdrop. In the winter, the greenhouse provides additional heat to the toolshed, giving it a comfortable place to work on chilly, rainy days.

Cooling

Evaporative coolers (also known as swamp coolers) are a low-maintenance, low-cost option for cooling buildings in hot, dry areas. In order to flow water through a swamp cooler, a tiny electric fan and a pump are used. The wind blows on the water that flows across the membrane. The evaporation of water cools the surrounding air (just like wearing a wet t-shirt on a windy day). As compared to air conditioners, evaporative coolers consume significantly less electricity. These, however, don't operate well in humid locations because of the humidity in the air.

As long as the sun doesn't strike directly on the floors, masonry floors can assist keep a place cool. Anyone who has ever spent time in a hot basement knows how uncomfortable it can be. Evaporative cooling can be enhanced by running misting sprinklers in an area with a lot of vegetation, such as a courtyard of a house, during hot weather.

A building's ability to maintain a comfortable temperature is greatly enhanced by strategically planted shade trees. Be sure to consider the species' mature size, the optimal location based on that size, the style of shade cast (dappled versus deep), and the suitability of the selected species with respect to the rest of the landscape when making your selection. Deciduous trees that are chosen for their leaf-out and leaf-drop dates can provide shade when needed and sun when desired, as opposed to an evergreen tree. In order to have both a well-lit interior and an effective environment under them, trees that shed light and dappled shadow are excellent selections. Thornless honeylocusts (Gleditsia triacanthos) and silk trees (Albizia julibrissin) make excellent shade trees in temperate areas. Consider monkeypod (Albizia saman) or narra in the tropics (Pterocarpus indicus). All of these trees fix nitrogen in the soil as well as provide shady cover.

Temperature moderation

There are ways to keep your building both warm in the winter and cool in the summer. Earth tubes, cisterns, and a lot of insulation are all part of the plan.

Tubes that are built underground near the building in which they are utilized are known as earth tubes (or ground-coupled heat exchangers). Subterranean temperatures of approximately 55°F can be found in most areas on Earth (with some variance for climate). Those tubes will therefore have identical temperatures. It'll be comfortable and cool inside your house if the air from those tubes is pushed directly into it on a hot summer day. On a chilly winter day, pumping the same air into a heating system uses less energy than pulling in outside air (which may need to be heated from 5°F to 68°F) to reach a pleasant temperature (55°F to, say, 68°F).

Because water is such an effective thermal mass, cisterns beneath buildings can help keep inside temperatures more comfortable throughout the year. You can save a significant amount of energy by putting a large tank of water beneath your home. A "thermal cistern" may retain heat from a heat source and radiate it back over an extended period of time if it is properly designed.

In addition, a well-insulated home can help keep the temperature down. In the winter, it can assist reduce heat loss through the floor, and in the summer, it can help keep the space cool. Ceilings, walls, windows and doors should also be insulated. Use weather-stripping around windows and doors to keep cold air out and heat in.

RETROFITTING BUILDINGS FOR HEALTH AND ENERGY EFFICIENCY

A healthy and energy-efficient home should be part of your initial preparations. Instead of beginning from scratch, what if your organization already has a solid foundation in place? Renovating your home instead of demolishing it would squander a significant amount of energy, negating the original motivation for doing so (not to mention that it would break the bank for most of us).

Choosing a place to live means balancing long-term goals with immediate needs. If your home was built within the previous decade and you have no plans to move very soon, you may want to consider retrofitting it to boost its efficiency and reduce its toxicity.

MEANS TO IMPROVE EFFICIENCY AND REDUCE TOXICITIES

	Making simple changes	Upgrading what you have	Adding new features
Toxicity and indoor air quality	Get houseplants (which can help to remove toxins from the air).	Repaint with low-or no-VOC paints or natural finishes. Remove carpet. Seal off openings to unfinished areas (such as crawl spaces).	Add good exhaust fans to rooms with moisture issues.
Thermal performance	Add weather stripping. Paint outside walls a light color to reflect the intense sun.	Increase wall insulation. Incorporate a thermal mass in a sunny spot.	Add or remove windows. Add earth tubes. Redo heating system. Build masonry heater.

Siting for fire Siting for wind Siting for sun	Cut firebreak. Add weather stripping. Put blinds outside windows that cause overheating.	Plant fire-resistant vegetation in the fire sector. Add insulation to the windward side. Build trellises on the sunny side. Modify eaves on the sunny side.	Install pond in the fire sector. Plant a windbreak windward. Lift and turn the building (can be feasible for small buildings). Build an attached greenhouse on the sunny side.

CHAPTER 8
DESIGNING THE PERMACULTURE GARDEN

Which of these high permaculture ideals will you try to put into practice in your own garden? The first step in starting a garden is to analyze your land and the surrounding area and to become familiar with the gardening conditions in your area. If your location, needs, and understanding of the site are taken into consideration, you can then form an overarching vision for the project. An idea for your garden can then be developed, and lastly, a workable plan can be created for your garden.

Sectors and zones are two distinct approaches used in permaculture to analyze and design your place. In reality, these terms are just common sense tools to help you organize your thoughts and, eventually, the garden vision you have in mind.

Evaluation of Your Garden

If you're trying to figure out how much garden space you have, consider these factors. To help you with your design and final planting selections and to keep your memories fresh, keep as many (dated) notes, photos, and videos as you can.

LOCATION

The first step is to determine where you are in relation to other people. If you've ever tended a garden, you know that latitude has a direct impact on how much sunlight it receives throughout the year. Summer and winter solstices and equinoxes are critical knowledge to consider when laying out a garden, as are spring and fall. Many edible plants cannot be grown in the desert since the sun is directly overhead for most of the day. You may want to focus on producing shadows initially. You should look for places where you may remove obstructions to increase the amount of sunshine available. Choosing plants that can tolerate short days and short seasons, cold winter temperatures and spring/fall frosts are also important considerations to make during the planting process. Tender plants and seedlings can necessitate the use of a greenhouse or cold frame.

PERMACULTURE IN COLD-WINTER CLIMATES

Even if your growing season only lasts for a hundred and twenty days of the year and your winter temperatures plummet to the single digits and below, you can still have a permaculture garden. Here are a few pointers for designing a garden for the winter:

- Short-season variety should be your first choice.
- Root crops can be grown for winter storage, and transparent materials like glass and plastic can be used to capture and store heat.
- Why do the harsh weather conditions in cold climates typically lead to poor soil? Soil quality can be improved by adding a lot of organic matter and using cover crops.
- Mulch frequently and a lot.
- Planting at the bottom of slopes, where cold air flows downhill, should be avoided.

- A frost trap can be created by planting a triangle-shaped hedge with the point facing up the slope at the base of a slope.
- Plant tender indicator plants like nasturtium in your yard and see which ones do best in cold weather to find the cold and hot spots on your property.
- Planting sensitive plants against south-facing walls can help trap heat for them.
- Young, fragile plants benefit from the shade provided by deciduous trees, such as quaking aspen. During the cool nights of late summer and October, the fluttering leaves of the aspens provide a pleasant filtered shade.
- Grow vegetables like melons and eggplants by covering the soil with black plastic mulch.
- Shelterbelts (barriers) should be built on the garden's north side.
- Late-season crops like carrots, collards, kale and parsley benefit from piles of leaves collected in the fall.
- Keep an eye on your plants in the winter. Seeds from plants that are better able to withstand cold conditions should be collected and stored.
- In the event of late or early frosts, protect young plants by covering them with cardboard boxes, row covers, or old bedsheets

PERMACULTURE IN HOT CLIMATES

There are two problems that plants encounter in hot, arid climates: too much sunlight and not enough liquid water. Here are a few tips for getting the most out of your garden when the weather is bad.

- Find plants that flourish in desert conditions by exploring zone 5, the wilderness. They need to be well-established and able to tolerate periods of prolonged dryness.

- Plant mesquite trees in the understory to protect more recognizable veggies and fruits. The tasty pods of this nitrogen-fixing tree attract pollinators.
- A windbreak of native hedges can reduce the drying effects caused by wind.
- For traditional food crops that grow well in the area, look to indigenous tribes. Tucson, Arizona-based seed firm Native SEED/Search specializes in both low and high-desert types.
- The Southwest Hopi tribe has evolved numerous maize types, including 'Hopi Greasy Head,' 'Wekte,' and others. So that the seeds have a natural covering of soil above them, plant these corn kinds deep—up to 18 inches.
- Cacti are capable of producing a wide range of crops. Cholla cactus flower buds can be preserved by drying, pickling or roasting and taste like asparagus. A tasty red or yellow fruit is produced by prickly pears, which are also known as tunas, and the immature pads are used to make nopales, a common Mexican ingredient.
- For inspiration, look to desert cultures around the world. Traditional Middle Eastern gardeners often use date palm trees as a tall tree layer providing shade in their landscapes. Apricots, Chinese dates (jujube), figs, mulberries, olives, and peaches fill out the understory. The shrub layer is completed with pomegranates and citrus fruits.
- Use water harvesting techniques to keep water on your property by slowing, spreading, and sinking the seasonal flow.
- It's best to plant in the rainy season so that the roots have time to establish themselves before the hot, dry season arrives.
- Be careful when designing your building. Internal courtyards with multistory structures or shade fabric for single-story buildings can be used to create a shady environment. To grow plants and fruit in pots below an arbor, you can cover it with grapes.

- When drying tomatoes and other fruits and vegetables, utilize the roof as the warmest spot on the property. Use window screens or floating row covers to keep birds and insects out of the dried food.
- The ground should be extensively mulched, and trees should be planted in courtyards to create cool, moist microclimates.
- To maximize water retention, use sunken beds rather than elevated ones. You can plant trees in mulched pits or cover the young plants with a thick layer of mulch (sheet mulching involves covering the ground with layers of organic matter). Stack pebbles around the tree trunk to keep mulch away from the trunk.
- In order to keep water from evaporating, it's best to water at night or early in the morning.

THE PATH OF THE SUN

Winter and summer gardening requires an understanding of the sun's passage across the sky. Determine if any structures or large trees are obstructing the sun's rays from reaching the regions where you intend to plant food. As a general rule, in the Northern Hemisphere, you should plant the tallest levels of the food forest to the north and lower layers to the southern end.

SOIL

The foundation of gardening is healthy soil, and good food cannot be grown without it. However, no matter how bad your soil is, it may be improved upon. You need to know what you're working with if you want to improve your soil. It is likely that your soil falls into one of the three general categories: sandy, clay, or loam. For the most accurate information on your soil, have it tested by a commercial laboratory. The percentage of mineral nutrients, pH, and the presence or absence of pollutants can be found here. In order to check if your soil is acidic or alkaline, you can purchase affordable pH strips. Most minor mineral deficits can be remedied by composting, mulching, and planting nitrogen fixers and nutrient accumulators. The results of a soil test will show whether or not amendments are essential if your soil is seriously deficient.

EXISTING PLANTS

Keep an eye out for the positioning and size of existing trees and how they may affect your landscape in the years to come. When a fast-growing eucalyptus tree or a coniferous evergreen tree takes over the entire yard, a sun-loving vegetable garden becomes impossible. Remove or maintain only those that are worthy of preservation. When trees are young, it's preferable to remove them before they become a problem. Call an arborist if you have any doubts about the health of a large tree. If you have a huge tree, a competent arborist can help you estimate its age and health, as well as locate a mill to process the wood. Always save the wood for compost and fuel. You may also use it to build raised beds. A school garden or plant swap may be a good place to donate tiny ornamental plants that don't fit into your overall landscape plan.

For inspiration on how to re-create ecosystems in your garden, have a look at your local native plant groups. In your near vicinity, what kinds of native plants can you find? What are their seasonal and climate adaptations? Is there a native plant that you can eat in your area? It is recommended by Bill Mollison that one begin with native plant foods before moving on to exotic ones. There are many advantages to using native plants over non-native ones, including the ability to attract local pollinators and the ability to plant in regions where other plants won't survive. As a pollinator shelterbelt and noise buffer, I've planted sun-loving natives in the dry curb strip and shade-loving natives on the north side of my house.

Sectors

The garden's relationship to the surrounding environment can be better understood through the use of sector diagrams. Sectors can be everything that has an impact on your garden, from the sun, wind, rain, or even an overly chatty next-door neighbor. There are certain wild energies that are welcome, such as sunlight in the winter and refreshing breezes in the summer. Some natural disasters, such as floods, frigid winter winds, sleet and fog, or fire dangers, can be avoided with proper landscaping. Are you near a body of water, such as the ocean? Depending on the weather, this could imply that your garden is vulnerable to salt-laden breezes or a moderating marine impact. Are there any seasonal weather occurrences, such as cold winter winds, if you are located inland? Is there a rain shadow or fog trapping mountain range nearby? Pollinators and pests may be drawn to your garden from adjacent wetlands, wild lands, and animal habitats. Is there a local recommendation to defend against brush fires by creating a buffer zone?

As a next step, take a step back and consider your site in terms of its many sections. What's the exact measurement? If so, what are the borders of the property like? What's going on in and around the location right now? Where does water run off into your yard? What are the most heavily traveled routes or driveways? Take a look at your neighbors' properties as well as your own garden.

When it comes to defining your personal space, how far are you willing to go? Does the area have any trees or buildings that could provide shade? You could want to check if there are any nearby vacant properties that could provide wind-borne weeds or even beneficial insects. Neighbors will see your garden in a different light than you, and vice versa. Do you have to think about any zoning difficulties or setbacks?

Your garden's elevations are also significant. Watch out for low places that may be prone to flooding if not dealt with properly. Low-lying places, as well as mountains, are affected by the movement of the snow. Temperatures are higher on the south and west-facing slopes. A problem with erosion could arise if there are any very steep slopes in the area.

An accurate map of the physical terrain can be created by sketching out all of the many features and objects that can be found there. Draw numerous sectors on tracing paper and place them on top of it. You can begin to see how the various sectors interact with one another and with the garden itself.

SECTORS

Planning your garden around the wild energy and elements that may affect it can be aided by creating sector maps on your land.

RAISED LOG BED

Small drainage issues in the garden can be solved using raised beds. Water will be able to drain away from your plants' roots more easily if you have a height of 6 to 12 inches. Using tree-cutting logs, you can create a border around a planting area. Fill the inside of the container with soil and compost in large quantities. It is possible to create a garden bed of any size and shape using logs, therefore maximizing the amount of room in the garden.

Water in the Garden

A garden's water supply is a critical consideration. Depending on the type of soil, you need to know how well your soil drains. Drainage on sandy soil is faster, but clay drains much slower. A percolation test replicates months of rain or a heavy storm to analyze how water drains through your soil. Time how long it takes for the water to drain out of a few 1-foot-deep holes dug around the prospective garden site. You're in luck if the hole drains rapidly. Compost and mulch will be necessary if it takes an hour. This indicates compacted or clayey soil. Poorly draining soil can be alleviated by using raised beds. Water infiltration or other methods may be required for more serious drainage issues.

WATER HARVESTING

You should keep an eye out for any running water, such as brooks, creeks, or streams. Is there a source of water beneath the land? Any seasonal natural water features, such as a dry creek or a vernal pool, can be observed over time in your landscape. Look for areas where water collects or rushes off the property if you can walk outside after a strong rainstorm. Water can be harvested from rooftops using catchment systems. It's possible to waste hundreds of gallons of rainwater every year, even in low-rainfall locations. Downspouts can direct water to cisterns, rain barrels, tanks, or onsite swales and pools, among other options.

Any wastewater from home, excluding toilet waste, can be used to collect greywater from the interior of the building. There are many different kinds of greywater systems, ranging from simple, low-cost systems to complex, high-cost systems. Prior to disposal, advanced systems use tanks and sand filters to separate particles and pathogens from greywater. You should check with your local building department before installing a greywater system to see if there are any local codes controlling greywater. In the event that you need to perform sewer system maintenance, ensure sure you have a valve that allows water to flow back into the sewer system.

There is a common belief that the fastest way to remove stormwater from a site is using conventional drainage methods. This can lead to soil erosion and the transport of silt into waterways via sewage systems. Earth-forming basins, dry streams, pools, and swales are all examples of water infiltration techniques that can be used to slow down and catch runoff. The goal is to slow, disperse, and sink the runoff throughout the land by directing water down the longest course feasible. The soil functions like a sponge, soaking up rainwater and storing it for the plants to use at a later date.

It is possible to utilize sunken beds to collect rainwater in arid climates. 6 inches of soil should be dug out of the garden beds. It is time to plant and mulch in the sunken hole.

Building A Swale

It is important to dig swales on the contour with level bottoms to ensure that water percolates uniformly. The contour line, an imaginary line that is level throughout the slope, must be found in order to accurately locate a swale on a slope. The most efficient way to block water from flowing through a swale is to place it exactly along the contour. Swale excavated soil piles up on the side of the ditch that is lower in elevation. Permanent plants can be used to support the soil around this berm.

There is no substitute for actually measuring the contour lines. A weighted A-frame level is a useful handmade tool for tracing contour. This is made up of three A-shaped poles that have been joined together. Put some thread around a small rock, then attach the other end of it to the top of the A-frame so that the weight may swing freely. Make a mark on the crossbar with a piece of twine by putting the frame on level ground. This is where you're at in terms of skill level. Locate places throughout the slope that are level and flag them with a flag.

Instructions

1. Use flags and an A-frame to draw a contour line on a slope of no more than 3:1.
2. The trench should be 3 feet broad, and 1 foot deep, and the excavated earth should be piled on top of each other to create a berm.
3. Flood the swale with a garden hose once you've determined the trench is level. You'll be able to plainly observe where the

water is low and high. Finish mounding soil downward with this method.

4. Add 6 inches of tree cuttings to the trench.
5. The mound should be topped with a layer of compost.
6. It's time to fill in the berm with vegetation.
7. Add a final layer of 2 inches of straw, 1 inch of sawdust, or 4 inches of tree trimmings to the trench and berm.

TRENCH COMPOSTING

Traditional hillside agricultural practices in Central America include trench composting as an alternative to traditional swales. Rather than following a contour, these swales have a trench that is deeper and wider than the average swale. In the first six inches of the trench, organic debris such as kitchen trash, coffee grinds, or horse manure is deposited. Over the course of a year, these stores of organic matter will decay into completed compost.

To finish the trench, a layer of woodchips, straw, or some other type of mulch is spread over the surface. It's possible to move the trench slightly downhill, mulching the existing perennials and trees, in the following year. To get around the garden, I like to use these excavations as a network of pathways. Another method of capturing water is to use deadwood swales. Dig a shallow trench and set logs where the berm will be erected after identifying the swales with an A-frame and flags. Bury the logs in the trench as you work on the swale's construction. As the wood rots, it becomes a sponge, soaking up rainwater. Carbon can be stored in the soil for a long time in the form of buried wood.

Designing Your Garden

Consider how your garden will be used on a daily basis. The place where you'd want to hang out? Yes, I would want to plant herbs near the kitchen. Is it possible to have raised beds? Regardless of whether or whether you are ready to build a shed, chicken coop, goat enclosure, greywater system, or beehive, will you have any structures at this time? Permaculture provides a way to think about the garden in terms of zones, which can assist you in deciding where to grow and build.

PERMACULTURE ZONES

The six permaculture zones are the finest planning tool for laying out a little garden. Think of the ripples that form when a small rock is tossed into a pond and how they spread outward in a circular pattern. Zones in permaculture work in a similar way, although the boundaries between zones are less defined and might overlap depending on the elements of the site already in place. Using zones to organize your garden makes it easier to decide where to put certain items based on how often they are used and their size. Zones 0, 1, and 2 are common in most average-sized home gardens, but with some imagination, we might imagine different zones even in smaller residential gardens.

The 0 zones are designated as a representation of one's own personal space. Zone 0 reminds us to begin the design process by observing our own inner landscapes," says Bonita Ford, a permaculture designer and teacher. Design and implementation are influenced by our personal beliefs, needs, likes, and dislikes. As living components of the design, the invisible/social parts of our work necessitate that we maintain our own life and originality. If we aren't taking care of ourselves, then we won't be able to maintain a garden. Out of the five zones, Zone 1 is the closest to the living area and receives the most use, while Zone 5 is the furthest away and receives the least use. It's a symbol of the wild. We may need to plant here in order to re-establish native habitats or to attract pollinating insects.

We want to be able to get our hands on the freshest and most frequently harvested fruits and vegetables right here at home. A typical annual planting schedule would look like this:

- **ZONE 1:** herb garden and salad mixes
- **ZONE 2:** frequently picked collards, kale, and Swiss chard
- **ZONE 3:** tomatoes or potatoes
- **ZONE 4:** amaranth, fava beans, mushrooms, sunflowers, and winter squash
- **ZONE 5:** native plants

STRUCTURES

Structures (sheds, greenhouses, arbors, fences, and gates) and infrastructure (irrigation and lighting) can be placed in the garden based on zone designations. Keep in mind that the order in which elements should be placed depends on the amount of energy used, how often it is cleaned, and the amount of input and output. Even though rain barrels can be placed in numerous different zones, the following is an example of a garden structure layout:

- **ZONE 1:** seating and dining areas, small greenhouse, cold frames, trellis, patio, compost bin, worm compost bin, nursery table, rain barrel
- **ZONE 2:** large greenhouse, tool shed, wood storage, chicken coop, beehives, well, swales, greywater
- **ZONE 3:** windbreaks, firebreaks, small ponds, workshop, storage, drip irrigation
- **ZONE 4:** swales, wood lot, nut trees, barn, pasture, large ponds
- **ZONE 5:** native habitat, wildlife corridors, river, wild berries, wetlands

INPUTS AND OUTPUTS

Individuals in the natural world benefit from their proximity to each other in complimentary pairings. It is possible to use the trash of one entity to supply food for another. Symbiotic relationships between plants and inedible trash are exemplified by compost. "We set up functioning relationships between each element so that the requirements of one element are supplied by the yields of another one," Bill Mollison and Reny Mia Slay (another permaculture pioneer) explained.

The only way to ensure zero waste is to design a garden with closed systems that link inputs (needs) and outputs (products) (products or yields). For us, the essential linkage is that a vegetable garden's output fits our family and community's food needs. The permaculture garden, however, has many different closed systems that can be created.

To irrigate fruit plants and bamboo, for example, greywater from home can be channeled. In the same way, urine can be diluted and used to water the vegetable garden and orchard. Compost discarded plants' stems and leaves or feed them to the poultry or goats while harvesting edible and flowering plants. Using chickens to eat pests in the garden can leave nitrogenous manure in the soil, which improves the quality of the soil. It's also possible to build trellises for birds and mushrooms. When lettuces and other annual vegetables begin to bolt, you can save the seeds for the following year's salad garden by collecting them.

Through pleasant connections with the community and encouraging garden practices that yield more fertility and less labor over time, harvests can also be acquired in the spirit of people care.

VISION

At this point, it's time to let your creative juices flow when it comes to the design of your website. Gardening would be so much more fun if there were no restrictions. The best way to get started is to jot down all of your aspirations and priorities in a brainstorming session. What could be done to improve the garden? For example, do you want to cultivate gourmet herbs to use in the kitchen or medicinal herbs to make tea? Do you want to grow fresh fruit, tomatoes, grapes, or flowers for cutting? Pruning your fantasy design will be an option in the future, but for the time being, let it grow.

CONCEPT

Vision is the large image, while the concept is the process of breaking it down into smaller parts. Permaculture zones can help you decide where to put significant features like compost systems, poultry, a small plant nursery and greenhouse, rainwater collecting tanks and bicycle parking buildings, a pond and comfy seating spaces. To find the optimum locations for tall trees, fruiting shrubs, ground covers, beds of annuals and perennials, and mushrooms, revisit the food forest's tiers. What matters most is how the various systems work together to benefit each other's needs. Bamboo, rather than a traditional wall or fence, was an easy and cost-effective way for me to conceal the nearby structures.

At the concept stage, it's a good idea to get in touch with your neighbors. Gardeners from other eras, cultures, and geographic places may be able to recommend plants you've never tried before. Someone is probably creating trash that you can recycle. The grass clippings from across the street are donated to my compost pile by a landscaper I know. My chickens and ducks get treats from other neighbors, and their grandchildren often come to visit our tiny sanctuary to see it.

ACTION PLAN

It's at this point that you come up with a final blueprint and budget. Think of it as a road map to help you find your way. An action plan outlines the who, what, where, and how of your permaculture garden. Create a design that is as detailed as feasible. Instead of putting "flowers, vegetables, and fruit," identify or list the specific varieties, you wish to grow and the plant sizes you want to plant.

Making progress on your garden will be much easier once specifics are in place.

Your inventory might look like this:

- 3 (4-inch) 'Munstead' lavender
- 6 (4-inch) tree collards
- 4 (4-inch) 'Egyptian Walking' onions
- 1 (3-gallon) 'Hayward' kiwi
- 1 (15-gallon) 'Hachiya' persimmon.

Also include design elements and their sizes, such as:

- 150-square-foot pond
- 500 square feet of vegetable beds
- 25 heritage breed chickens (such as Rhode Island Red, Barred Rock, or Australorp).

Staged implementation is the way to go. To begin, remove any trees and plants you no longer desire and use the carbon harvested for fuel, construction, mushroom cultivation, compost, or hugelkultur. Create drainage canals and swales. Start sheet mulching to smother the grass and make use of the nitrogen it delivers as it decomposes if you have a large area of lawn to convert. See if you can borrow goats or sheep for a few weeks or repeatedly sheet mulch and remove the undesired weeds from your garden. Truck in compost and woodchips if necessary to enrich the soil.

Fences raised beds, and trellises can all be constructed. Make sure your irrigation and greywater recycling systems are up and running before you begin using them. You should follow a logical sequence when you are ready to plant. In order of maturation, beginning with the deepest layer first. Shelterbelts can be used as windbreaks in windy areas to help the establishment of anything downwind.

As the surrounding strata are gradually filled up, there will initially be space between the larger plants. Planting annual vegetables like brassicas, lettuce, radishes, and salad greens will help keep weeds out of the lower tree and shrub levels.

An ecological garden's plant succession also changes with time, just like the demography of a particular city or neighborhood. After the fruit and nut trees have matured, David Holmgren suggests starting edible forest gardens with 25 percent nitrogen fixers and then trimming them back to be less of a presence. There is no need to bring in fertilizer for the first season because beans and peas are nitrogen-fixers. Do not stop cultivating plants that draw minerals from deep within the earth.

RE-EVALUATION

All the different aspects of your permaculture design should be reevaluated annually to make sure that they weave into a cohesive whole. Moving a few struggling plants to a better site or improving the drainage are examples of little alterations and fixes that can be performed. As a result, your cycle begins over each year with an assessment, vision, concept, action plan, and evaluation.

Re-evaluating permaculture designs on a regular basis ensures that they are dynamic, unique, and site-specific and that they may evolve to best match the environment, your plants and human use patterns. Conventional garden designs tend to be static and two-dimensional, making them less dynamic. Season after season, the permaculture design process allows for direct participation in the design.

ASSESSMENT

Map out the much wild energy that may affect your garden by tracing the boundaries of your property.

VISION PLAN

Let your creative juices flow here, and imagine the garden of your dreams. It's like looking out a window into your backyard.

CONCEPT PLAN

A general plan for the area might be drawn up in the concept phase, cutting back on concepts from the vision.

ACTION PLAN

Based on your vision and concept, you will flesh out the details of your action plan in this phase.

CHAPTER 9

BUILDING THE SOIL

SOIL BASICS

People and soil both bear the truth of the adage "you are what you eat." Only by feeding the soil can it maintain its health. The ethical notion of earth care and a passion for soil, soil building, and soil regeneration is at the heart of soil health.

The decomposition of rocks, plants, and animals over millions of years is what gives soil its texture. There are three types of soil: sand, clay, and loam, or a combination of the three. There are a variety of soil types. According to this definition, it relates to how soil holds together in terms of air, moisture and organic matter. Soil that has been saturated with water might become compacted when dug. A lack of water causes soil to convert into a fine powder.

Digging into a well-structured soil yields pea-sized fragments, making it easier to work with. A single inch of topsoil in a natural forest can take up to a thousand years to accumulate. Eventually, if there are no plants or animals to decompose, the soil will become dead dust. A diverse community of soil-dwelling species relies on plants to convert sunlight into green biomass, which in turn is devoured by a wide range of other living things, such as microorganisms, protozoa, nematodes, insects, and birds. The greatest way to grow healthy plants is to maintain diversified and healthy soil.

By eliminating the natural cycle of matter and energy, modern agriculture has resulted in an alarming depletion of topsoil. Bioneers founder Kenny Ausebel estimates that European-style plow agriculture has destroyed 75% of the continent's topsoil.

We can't expect good food to come from soil that has been mined to the bone. Organic material from plants and animals must be constantly reintroduced into the soil in order for our gardens to be really sustainable. Our gardening and agricultural practices have a significant impact on soil health and can either deplete or enrich it. The natural processes of composting, mulching, utilizing cover crops, rotating crops, and adding compost tea all contribute to the soil food web's enrichment because of this. It's simple to learn how to do this, and the end result is good soil for our delicious gardens.

COMPOST

So many permaculture concepts can be found in composting, such as working with nature, producing no waste, making the most out of what you have and valuing what you have—tough it's to envision sustainable gardening without it. When plants die, fruit, leaves, stalks, or blossoms fall to the ground, where they are broken down by soil-dwelling insects and microorganisms and then used as food for the next generation, creating a food web in the soil.

Compost Basics

Creating a compost pile requires the addition of four elements: green (wet) material, brown (dry) material, air and water. One-third of the material should come from kitchen scraps; another third should be made from green material; the remaining third should be made from brown material; this should be done while ensuring that the material is not too wet or too dry for proper circulation (the whole pile should be as damp as a wrung-out sponge). Putrid compost can be caused by too much green material or water in the mix.

The lack of biological decomposition is caused by an abundance of air. As a result, the pile will not get hot. It's just like any other recipe: practice is required to get the proportions just right.

There are a number of factors to consider when deciding on the size of your compost bin. This bin can be harvested several times per year because it's easy to create and requires the least amount of turning. Processing kitchen scraps on a regular basis are easy with this machine. Compost can be turned more regularly in stackable plastic bins, making for faster output. If you have the room and want to flip piles, the three-bin method (three 3-cubic-yard wooden bins in a row) is a great option.

An alternative composting method is windrows, a lengthy, winding pattern made of stacked and laid-down materials. They are picked once or twice a year and do not rotate. For the home gardener, windrows can only be used if you have a lot of space and a reliable supply of green and brown materials.

Shade and a strong layer of covering are essential for compost in dry or hot areas. Mulch and tarps can be used to cover the pile. If you live in a cold area, zone 1 or 2 can be a good choice because you don't want to have to wade through a lot of snow to get to the pile. Straw bales can be used to prevent piles from freezing. The accumulation of big snowdrifts on top can be prevented by placing a removable wooden lid on the pile. Those who live in rainy regions should take precautions to keep their belongings dry. It will become anaerobic and produce a foul odor if the pile is too damp.

Building the Compost

Office paper and home-grown vegetable scraps will be found in some piles, while leaves, animal manure, and garden clippings may be found in others. Adding additional variety to your compost can yield a better result in the long run. To increase the size of your compost pile, go beyond your own backyard. You may be able to help out places like grocery stores, juice bars, coffee shops, restaurants, and food banks by offering to pick up their bad produce. There may be an abundance of manure on farms or stables.

Inquire about your neighbors' composting habits, and if they do not, offer to take their cooking scraps if they do not already do so. Just be sure to collect up their compost regularly. Using permaculture principles, you're illustrating how garbage may be transformed into a sustainable food source. You should give back to people who have helped you out if you have a large harvest.

Build up your pile by layering browns with kitchen and garden produce until it reaches 3 feet high. Wet the pile to the consistency of a wrung-out sponge in between each layer. Continually add 4-inch layers of greens and 2-inch layers of browns every few weeks to keep the color scheme fresh. With a garden fork, you can hasten the decomposition of the pile. As the material decomposes in a well-designed compost pile, heat is generated. It's best to keep the temperature between 130 and 150 degrees Fahrenheit. Maintaining this temperature for a week will destroy many weed seeds and diseases.

When the compost looks and smells like finished decaying, you know it's ready to use. A dark, earthy hue and a deep, sweet aroma will be the result of the absence of any identifiable constituents, such as vegetable scraps and straw.

Brown Compost Materials

- Woodchips
- Wood shavings
- Straw
- Spoiled hay
- Sawdust (avoid plywood and treated wood)
- Office paper

- Newspaper
- Dried leaves
- Dried crop residues like sunflower stalks or chaff from seed winnowing
- Cardboard

Green Compost Materials

- Tea bags and leaves
- Seaweed
- Restaurant trimmings
- Manure (chicken, cow, goat, horse, rabbit, and sheep)
- Kitchen scraps
- Juice pulp
- Grass clippings
- Garden weeds (without mature seeds or perennial roots)
- Fish bones
- Crop residue (such as spent tomato vines)
- Cover crops
- Compost crops like comfrey
- Coffee grounds
- Animal bedding (chicken, cow, goat, horse, rabbit, and sheep)

Carbon-To-Nitrogen Ratio

Bacteria are carbon-based and nitrogen-fueled organisms. You want to encourage the growth of the bacteria that will break down your kitchen trash and straw into compost, which requires a ratio of carbon to nitrogen (C:N) of 30 to 1.

Carbon-To-Nitrogen (C:N) Ratio Greens

- Fish scraps 5:1
- Chicken manure 7:1
- Fresh grass clippings 12:1
- Cow manure 18:1

- Seaweed 19:1
- Used coffee grounds 20:1
- Restaurant trimmings 25:1
- Kitchen scraps 25:1
- Horse manure 25:1
- Fresh leaves 30:1
- Garden weeds 30:1
- Juice pulp 35:1

Browns

- Hay 25:1
- Dry leaves 50:1
- Dried crop residues like corn stalk 60–75:1
- Straw 75–125:1
- Woodchips 100–500:1
- Newspaper 175:1
- Cardboard 350:1
- Sawdust 500:1

The C:N ratios of various composts can be gauged using the information in the table below. In the absence of a calculator, I know to use sawdust carefully if I discover that dry leaves are 50:1 C:N while sawdust is 500:1. The ratios of horse manure and kitchen leftovers are 25:1; therefore, I make extensive use of both of them. Grass clippings (12:1) and chicken manure (7:1), on the other hand, are sparingly applied in thin layers by me.

Red Worm Composting

Vermiculture is the process of transforming organic materials into finished compost using a red worm farm. A main decomposer found in soil, Eisenia fetida, or red worms, feed on leaf litter and manure. They are also known as composting worms, red wigglers, tiger worms, and gourmet worms.

Vermiculture generates no trash, making it an excellent choice for those who have limited room for composting or who dislike the thought of turning compost by hand. The final product, worm castings, is a potent plant fertilizer that is highly concentrated. Your plants will be more fertile and nutrient-rich, thanks to the beneficial enzymes and microorganisms in this product. The red worms actually digest the material multiple times. In the words of the Worm Lady of the East Bay, Claudia Taurean, "(red worms) consume what they live on and live in what they eat." In just six months, eight adult worms can produce 1500 offspring. Extra worms can be given to relatives and friends, sold, or fed to the hens and ducks.

Red worm bins can be fashioned from a variety of containers, including food-grade tubs that have been recovered. Punch or drill holes towards the top of each side (but not on the lid). Bedding such as shredded newspaper should be placed inside. For every pound of red worms, at least 3½ pounds of material is consumed each week. In addition to bedding, food trash, eggshells, and coffee grounds are all fair game. Don't include any animal by-products, milk fats, butter, sugar, citrus peels, or onion peels. The ideal vegetable-to-fruit ratio for composting is 2:1 to prevent the material from becoming overly acidic. Cover kitchen scraps with newspaper or dried leaves for 6 inches to keep flies away. The worms can become poisoned by the castings if you don't collect them frequently enough.

Locating a bin is critical. The worms will perish if you place them in direct sunlight. During the winter, store the trashcan in a well-ventilated area to avoid freezing. 55° to 77° F is the optimal temperature range. Avoid frost damage to the bin by putting it under a tall evergreen tree or shrub. My worm bins are located near the main composting system in a sunny area with easy access to a path. With the bin in the garden, it's simple to collect the castings.

Castings and worm juice can be harvested after two months from the bottom of the bin; in order to remove the live red worms from the liquid, flush the bin with water. Return the red worms to the bin with new bedding and a constant supply of food. For your garden, you can use the liquid as a nutrient tea as a natural fertilizer. Ten parts water to one part juice is a good rule of thumb for diluting worm juice to the color of tea (not coffee). Pour the tea around the base of your plants as soon as it's made, using a watering can. Compost tea, on the other hand, is even richer in nutrients. You should only use about 10% of the entire volume of fresh worm castings as soil fertilizer in containers or garden beds if you want to get the best results. However, if you don't mix them with compost or cover them with mulch, castings will dry out and form a hard crust.

Outdoor bins need to be protected against raccoons, opossums, rats, and snakes, all of whom are known to like worms and food scraps. Keeping a brick on the top of your worm bin or covering the outside with hardware cloth or chicken wire is a simple way to do this.

MULCH

Soil quality can be improved by studying forest ecosystems, which do it all the time. There aren't any landscapers around to pick up the discarded leaves, twigs, and branches when they fall. Because they act as a barrier to keep the soil from drying out or eroding, however, they aren't necessary. In the end, worms and other soil creatures help them decompose so that they can be used as food for future growth. Mulching in the garden mimics this on-site recycling.

There are only 22 inches of rain per year in my garden in northern California, and most of it falls from November to May. The sun bakes the clay soil into adobe if it is left exposed during the dry summers, making digging like working with concrete. Moist and workable soil can be maintained by applying a layer of mulch (at least 4 inches per year). The soil food network is alive and well, and you can watch it in action. In addition to protecting crops from weeds, maintaining soil moisture, and increasing soil fertility as it decomposes, mulch is a labor-saving technique. Mulching with wood chips is one of my favorite gardening methods because I hate weeding. Slugs, snails, and scavenger insects are the only downsides of mulch. Plants that are still growing need to be protected from winter snow and ice, so keep the mulch away from them in the spring.

Bark, cardboard, finished compost, grass clippings, leaves, newspaper, straw, ruined hay, tree trimmings, well-rotted manure, and woodchips are all good mulching materials (not pressure treated and not from plywood).

Making Compost Tea

Soil and water are the main ingredients in composting. Using an aquarium bubbler, the mixture is cultured for three days before it is ready to be used as a foliar spray on your plants. This spray is full of vitamins, minerals, and helpful bacteria and yeasts that your plants will love. Certain illnesses can be prevented, and plants damaged by pests can recover with the help of tea.

Materials

- garden pump sprayer
- fabric paint strainer
- aquarium bubbler
- Water
- 6 cups of molasses
- 1 pound of red worm castings or 4 cups of red worm tea
- 5-gallon bucket

Instructions

1. Place red worm castings or tea in the bucket and add 3 gallons of water.
2. Add molasses, and stir.
3. Insert aquarium bubbler; leave for three days.
4. Strain through a fabric paint strainer and pour into a pump sprayer. Apply immediately to plants. Compost tea is good for only one day.

Apply the tea on a calm day when there is no wind. Cover the plant's leaves on both sides if possible. Wear goggles and a mask to keep spray out of your eyes and mouth.

Sheet Mulching

When it comes to sheet mulching, the components you use are determined by what is accessible in your area. You'll need some cardboard or newspaper to get started. Make sure you remove any staples and packaging tape when you buy large cardboard boxes from bike shops or furniture stores. Magazine glossy paper should be avoided. If a soil test indicates them, you'll also require amendments. Feathers, blood, rock dust and seaweed are just a few examples of the many ingredients that can be used in animal feed. Any animal dung will do, whether it's from a chicken, goat, horse, or rabbit. Lastly, you'll want to include additional organic waste, such as kitchen scraps, brewer's waste, coffee grounds, pulp from juicers, municipal compost, old potting soil, straw or leaves from trees, and woodchips, bark, or sawdust. Plywood and pressure-treated wood are off-limits. A solid balance of greens and browns is essential for a diverse color scheme.

It's important to thoroughly smother the underlying material and therefore pile the components on top of one another. Sheet mulching a wider area and spreading it out too thin is preferable to starting with a small area and spreading it out to a depth of 12 inches. If you want to grow a variety of crops, you can change the mix to suit your needs. Horse dung and straw can be used to speed up the decomposition of annuals in the garden. The decomposition rate of woodchips, tree clippings, and sawdust is lower than that of soil; hence they're better for plants.

Fall sheet mulching and spring planting provide optimal results. Individual plantings such as potatoes, tomatoes, squash, and other large transplants can also be amended with finished compost prior to being placed in a sheet-mulched area.

Instructions

1. Water the area to be mulched for several hours.
2. Cut down existing vegetation and leave the trimmings or grass clippings in place.
3. Spread appropriate amendments, if needed.
4. Put down 1 inch of cardboard or several layers of newspaper, overlapping each section.
5. Water the cardboard or paper thoroughly.
6. Add a 9-inch layer of manure and organic waste.
7. Water once more.
8. Cap with a 2-inch layer of bark, sawdust, straw, or woodchips.
9. To plant immediately, move back some mulch and make an X in the paper layer. Dig a planting hole, add a shovelful of finished compost, and set the plant or seed in the hole. Replace the mulch around the base of the plant.

COVER CROPS

Planting cover crops is not for human consumption but rather for the benefit of the land. They are nursing crops that nourish the soil food chain by providing nitrogen, carbon, and other minerals as well as organic matter. Additionally, they operate as a living mulch, control weeds, and provide food and shelter for beneficial insects in the following season's crops. Soil structure and water absorption are improved because the full biomass of the cover crop plant, including roots, leaves, stems and fruits, is dug into the ground. N-fixing cover crops and dynamic accumulators are two of the most effective ways to supplement soil nutrition.

Cover crops, like sheet mulching, are excellent methods for establishing new garden beds. In the late fall, sow cover crops such as vetch, annual rye, and bell beans. Cut them down in the spring and either dig them in or mulch them. Planting this year's crops will be possible in a matter of weeks after decomposition and the release of nutrients.

Some gardeners like to retain some of their underused beds planted during the warm season with something that will enrich the soil for their fall crops. In the summer, I sow buckwheat or beans as a cover crop and wait two weeks before planting squash. Summer is the ideal time to grow cover crops in cooler climates so that crops can thrive in the following year.

CHAPTER 10

PERMACULTURE EDIBLES

When edible plants are placed in an environment they may thrive, they are referred to as "permaculture" or "ecological gardening." It is essential that you learn about a wide variety of annual and perennial edible plants, as well as how to plant, maintain, harvest, process, and share your harvests.

However, keep in mind that the ultimate goal is to let nature do the work for you. There are many different kinds of fruits and vegetables, and each one has its own cultural, regional, and seasonal attributes. A good starting point for creating guilds is to consider the similarities that edible plants may have, such as being members of the same plant family or native to a particular place or season or even being utilized in the kitchen in a similar manner. If you're looking for something new to try, you'll find a wide range of options. I've compiled a list of some of my favorite plants that can be grown in most parts of the country and are highly fruitful for a novice gardener. Most can be eaten fresh or preserved and have a wide range of cultural preferences.

Do not forget about the importance of paying attention to local growing circumstances in permaculture. From June through

September, most of the country is free of frost. However, in some locations, planting may be necessary as late as July to avoid late frosts. There are a few hardy crops that can be sown as early as April in other places.

Find out what grows well in your neighborhood and community gardens by talking to your neighbors and friends. Next, look for lectures, events, and other nearby informed experts through your local county cooperative extension office and Master Gardener groups.

Local nurseries can also help you figure out what flourishes in your area and when to seed or plant them. If you're not familiar with your local frost dates or the number of chilling hours, which are the number of continuous winter hours below 45° F, this kind of information is extremely useful. Chill hours in the coastal Bay Area normally total around 400, but in the inland areas, they can go as high as 900. It's impossible to grow some varieties of apples here that require as much as 1800 hours of sunlight.

Using and valuing diversity in our gardens is a permaculture principle that encourages us to experiment. If we want to thrive in our unique environment, we must learn from our failures and build on our triumphs. Growing conditions will vary slightly from year to year. A cold snap will kill a young seedling one year, while a hailstorm the following spring will destroy the blossoms on certain fruits. In order to be resilient when things go wrong but still have enough food, we must create a culture of joyful experimentation and maintain a diverse array of crops.

Fruits and Nuts

My oldest kid delights in picking her own fruit in the backyard. My daughter used to get in trouble for picking berries that were green or white when she was little. After a lot of practice, she has mastered the art of picking fruit at the right moment. Picking, tasting, and arranging fruit can keep her occupied for lengthy periods of time, which is something I really like. To meet the increasing needs of my growing family, I've increased the number of fruit trees in my yard. Sharing the seasonal fruit I've grown myself with friends and family is a wonderful feeling.

Your climate and taste preferences will obviously influence your selection of fruit trees, shrubs and vines. When it comes to citrus, Meyer lemons and pomegranates are popular in Florida and California, while heirloom apple varieties and locally created grapevines are more likely to thrive in Michigan and New York. Always keep an eye out for the signs of change and be prepared to act accordingly. You should keep growing a certain plant if it is producing well and you enjoy eating it. Next year, plant more blueberries if they're doing well this year. A nut tree can be a great addition to your yard, provided you have the room. The more you watch and experiment, the better you'll get.

Other critters drawn to your food garden can benefit from this observational approach as well. As tasty as these crops are, furry, feathery, and winged pests will no doubt try to eat them as well, so you'll need a few tactics and approaches to keep them out of your crops.

SHARING THE HARVEST

Since fruit harvests are typically too abundant for the average household to consume during their peak harvest season, permaculture encourages the practice of sharing. Because of their small size, wild plums are commonly referred to as "cherry plums" where I reside. There are several varieties. Birds and squirrels disperse the seeds across the city. Our backyard had a giant wild plum tree when we first moved here, so we had enough fresh plums to eat and share with neighbors. In one instance, I worked late one night to make 24 quarts of plum jam!

People who have fruit, in my experience, are willing to trade and share. You may be able to scavenge some of the unharvested fruit in your neighborhood with a little polite research and networking. Place names like the Pear Tree Shopping Mall in Palo Alto or the Fruitvale neighborhood in Oakland may reflect a community's agricultural history. The gnarled old trees in Moraga, California's old pear orchards are still being harvested by locals in the summer. Olive Drive, a street in Davis, California, is a gathering place for those who want to salt or brine their olives. Your town may also have yard-share or fruit-share groups.

Fruit trees are commonly used as ornaments in various regions. Crabapples are a typical landscaping plant in Michigan, where I grew up, but the fruit is rarely collected despite the trees' lovely blossoms and traditional shade tree shape. My mother and I would collect crabapples from the trees of our neighbors and make jelly out of them. As a newbie gardener, you may have to learn how to tell when a crop is ready for harvesting and eating.

Most street fruit is either harvested before it is ripe or eaten quickly before being thrown away. Some of my neighbors' fruit has been stolen from their front yard, including apples, plums, and peaches. A sign that reads, "Not ready!?" has now been erected. When it's ready, we'll send out a free box."

After harvesting the main crop, you can glean the fruit that is left over if permission has been granted by the farmer. This option is in line with the permaculture principle of fair share. Some time ago, a farmer in an olive grove not far from my home invited neighbors and friends to come to assist him in picking olives. Ten people showed up and spent the day picking olives, which was a lot of work. When the fruit was harvested, we each received a little over a gallon of olive oil from a local processing plant.

FRUIT TREES

Fruit trees are a study in patience and practice. Because it is the largest plant and necessitates the most forethought, a fruit tree serves as the centerpiece of a guild. When planning a new garden, start with semi-dwarf or dwarf trees and work your way out from there. There are ways around existing fruit trees, but they need you to deal with the current conditions in your area. A mature standard tree makes it difficult to plant under since those plants will be deprived of sunlight. Trees that are more than three years old can be thinned out to a height of 8 feet to make room for sun-loving plants below. It's also possible to lessen the danger of disease by thinning down the branches.

Hardiness, chilling hours, disease resistance, and pollination requirements are all things to keep in mind when making your final decision on which fruit tree variety to go with. Some trees are self-pollinating, whereas others necessitate a pollinator for their reproduction. A professional nursery will be able to tell you about a tree's pollination requirements. You might be able to use a neighbor's tree if you don't have the space for multiple varieties. As long as you have bees nearby, clipping flowering branches from an appropriate pollinator and putting them in a pot next to your tree will do the trick. Multi-variety trees with two or three different scions grafted onto one rootstock can be planted in small gardens.

In a short period of time, a lot of fruit can be harvested from a single tree. Managing an overflowing harvest can be time-consuming, so prepare ahead to eat, process or share what you harvest. It goes without saying that you should consume as much fresh fruit as possible because it is both beneficial to your health and delicious when eaten right after being gathered. Fruit can be preserved for the entire year by drying, canning, fermenting, or freezing it for use during the non-fruiting season. Then think of methods to trade what you have with family, friends, and neighbors in order to diversify your resources. Alternatively, you can practice your fair share by donating boxes of fruit to organizations that help feed the hungry, such as schools, food banks, and churches.

POME FRUITS

There are both known fruits like apples and pears, as well as more obscure ones like medlar and quince, in this group.

Apples

Most Americans love apples, which can be consumed as raw or cooked fruit; they can also be used to make juice or cider; they can be simmered, stewed, and baked. I'm particularly fond of their spring blooms, which announce the beginning of spring and draw bees to the yard. It's hard to believe there are hundreds of distinct apple kinds to choose from, but the Red and Golden Delicious, Fuji, Gala, and Granny Smith are just a few of the most well-known.

Apples aren't suited to hot climates because they don't tolerate high temperatures well. It's possible to grow a variety of fruiting plants throughout the year so that you'll always have a supply to eat. Apple scab, fireblight, and crown rot-resistant cultivars are also readily available. Choosing a rootstock that limits the height and spread of an apple tree is critical; search for semidwarf varieties that reach a maximum height of 15 feet. You can save space by growing columnar kinds that are ideal for pots and small gardens.

Pears

In comparison to apples, pears have a longer life span and are more resistant to pests. They're great as a dessert fruit, and canned versions are almost as tasty. Pears are a wonderful choice if you have clay soil because they are better able to withstand heavy soils than most fruits. In hot areas like California or Florida, Asian pears may be a better option than European pears, which require more winter frost and lower average temperatures. Grafting pear trees onto quince rootstock helps keep their height in check because pear trees naturally grow tall.

Other pome fruit

Quince is a lovely little tree that does well in a permaculture garden because of its adaptability. Most varieties of fruit cannot be eaten fresh, but they can be transformed into delicious jellies, chutneys, and jams when cooked. They have a longer shelf life and require less chilling time than other pome fruits.

An evergreen warm-climate fruit tree, the loquat, can be tried if the correct environment and area are available. This is one of those fruits that is hard to come by because of the fruit's poor storage and shipping characteristics. It's a small tree, only reaching a height of 15 feet, but pollination is impossible without at least two of them. It's a low-maintenance option that works well. White, yellow, or orange fruits are all delicious and tart, depending on the kind.

It is quite rare in North America to find a medlar tree, a typical European fruit tree. Persimmon-like in appearance, the fruit is harvested green and preserved for several weeks until the flesh becomes soft and pliable enough to consume (a ripening process known as bletting).

STONE FRUIT: APRICOTS, CHERRIES, NECTARINES, PEACHES, AND PLUMS

In late spring and early summer, these are the must-have sweets. The pit in the middle of the fruit gives stone fruits its name, and all of them have delicate scents, high sugar content, and soft flesh. Climate, microclimates, and soil all play a role in the success of stone fruit production. Choosing winter-hardy and late-blooming types is important in northern gardens, where early spring frosts can limit pollinating insects and harm early fruit. Fungal illnesses can be an issue in areas with humid temperatures, such as the Pacific Northwest and the South. Winter chilling hours are especially important in hotter climates.

Cherry

Sweet and sour cherries, sometimes known as pie cherries, are the most common types of cherry grown in gardens. Keep in mind that sour cherries can be eaten, but they are more commonly used in cooking and drying. Warmer climates are better suitable for growing sweet cherries. A pollinator is necessary for most cherry trees. Choose a rootstock that limits the size of the plant, as cherry trees can grow to 40 feet in time.

Plums

There are even more options if you want to produce plums. Asian plums, European plums, and hybrids of the two are all available. Fresh, dried jams and jellies, and even wine can be created from them. Prior to making a selection, be sure to double-check the pollination requirements and the rootstocks. It's possible to get wild plums or cherries in some places, and they're delicious. Local natural plums and cherries have been successfully grafted on by competent grafters to grow branded kinds in situations where ordinary rootstock would be unsuitable (such as in wet soils).

Apricot

The tart and sweet apricot are one of my favorite stone fruits. Pruning apricot trees in the summer rather than the winter is an exception to the rule for most deciduous fruit trees. On a commercial basis, these trees are chopped down every twenty years, so bear that in mind when you have an elder tree and wonder why it's not producing as much as you'd want. Harvests should be separated into those that can be eaten fresh and those that can be preserved for cooking, drying, or canning.

There are a variety of citrus fruits: grapefruit (a citrus fruit), lime (a citrus fruit), and orange (a citrus fruit).

Citrus trees, which flourish in hot climates, aren't likely to grow in every area. Citrus can be grown in containers or greenhouses in cooler climates. Even if you live in a warm region, you should still look for varieties and sorts that are appropriate. Citrus trees should be planted against a south-facing wall or covered with sheets or row covers to avoid frost damage. Mandarins are the most tolerant of citrus fruits to freezing temperatures.

I love Meyer lemons because they thrive in chilly summer climates and have a sweeter flavor than the usual lemon. For most of the year, you'll be able to pick fruit from this tree. Meyer lemons can be used in a variety of ways, including making lemonade, squeezing over salad greens, making lemon bars, or zesting spaghetti.

TREE TOMATO

Plants in the Solanaceae family—which includes tomatoes, peppers, and potatoes—are known as tree tomatoes (Cyphomandra betacea). About 20 feet tall, these are fast-growing trees. The fruit resembles tomatoes or tomatillos and can be used in a variety of ways, such as in soups, pasta dishes, or as a salad ingredient.

OTHER: AVOCADOS, FIGS, PERSIMMONS, POMEGRANATES, OLIVES, AND MULBERRIES

Just like in the world of fashion, there are fads in food crops. A few years ago, pomegranates were considered unusual, but now most people are aware of the health benefits of drinking their juice. Our agriculture system is built on a market economy. Instead of growing food, farmers cultivate mulberries to keep birds away rather than for their own consumption.

Mulberries, for example, can be grown on a smaller scale in a permaculture garden. However, you'll have to put up some sort of barrier against the birds.

Fast-growing and spreading, figs are a popular permaculture choice in warmer locations (although they can survive winter temperatures down to 10° F). A pergola or arbor can be used to train them, and they can yield two crops a year in some areas.

Pomegranates feature bright red blossoms and grow up to 20 feet tall naturally, but they can be trained to take on the shape of a tree with some pruning. Because they prefer a hot climate, they do best when planted against a south-facing wall in marginal regions, where the sun will help ripen the fruit in the fall. Pomegranates can be grown in large containers as well, of course.

When it comes to permaculture, persimmons are an excellent crop since they produce fruit well into the fall (November–December). In terms of winter sweetness, no other fruit comes close to persimmons. Tropical-looking trees, persimmons have glossy, dark green leaves and bright orange fruits that remain after the leaves have fallen like ornaments. Their ability to grow in the partial shade makes them an excellent understory tree. Fresh persimmons are too astringent to consume; therefore, they are allowed to mature on the tree until they are soft enough to handle. I've collected persimmons, dried some, and stored the rest in my freezer for the following summer, when I'll use them in fruit smoothies and do-nothing ice cream. Non-astringent varieties like 'Fuyu,' which can be eaten like apples, enhance in flavor when allowed to soften.

The only place you can grow avocados is in a climate without freezing temperatures. Omega-3 fatty acids, which are uncommon in plants, are found in these delicious and nutritious meals. You'll need two trees of the same type for pollination if you have an A and a B type, which opens at different times of the day. Avocado trees may grow up to 30 feet tall and broad, so they require a lot of food throughout the winter months to be healthy. Because of poor drainage, they either perish or fight. When the fruits are still hard, remove them from the tree and allow them to ripen.

NUT TREES

Most nut trees are large enough to be under the canopy, but there are a few uncommon dwarf varieties, like the filbert, that defy this rule. You should consider the size of your garden when putting in huge nut trees or planting around them, as you should when doing so with large fruit trees. Future preparation has long been valued by those who came before us. Every time a new church was built in the nineteenth century, an oak tree was planted as a legacy for future generations who would require the wood to restore the building. As with permaculture, we think about the future generations who will inherit our gardens and how we might provide them with sustainable food and resources.

When it comes to nut trees, you also have to consider how long the tree will take to bear fruit. Nuts can be harvested from some trees in as little as a year. Two to four years is all it takes for almonds to start bearing fruit. It can take up to ten years for some trees, such as stone pines, to begin producing and forty years for them to reach their full capacity. Almond, filbert, and walnut are some of the most popular tree nuts. Araucaria bidwillii (Araucaria bidwillii), hickory, chestnut, macadamia nut, oak, pecan, pinyon, and stone pine are some of the less frequent trees. A nut tree's success depends on where it is planted; there is no single tree that works well for everyone.

Go to farmers' markets and talk to other growers to find out what is being cultivated in your area.

Filberts, which can reach heights of 10 to 18 feet in cold areas, make excellent garden-scale nut trees. Coastal locations from northern California to British Columbia provide mild, moist winters and chilly summers with enough chill hours to support the growth of these plants.

Most almonds are cultivated commercially in California, which has a favorable climate for the crop. Even though almonds and peaches share a strong genetic relationship, it is difficult to cultivate them in locations with freezing winters because of their demand for hot summers. My favorite nut to grow is the 'All-In-One' almond. Winter hardiness and self-fruitfulness are two of its best qualities. However, in my growing coastal region, where summer heat appears to be sufficient for it to yield nuts, it doesn't normally require hot summers to ripen. Ripe soft-shell nuts crack open easily. Sweet and delicious, nutmeat is a treat to eat. Compared to other nut trees, it's a wonderful fit for smaller gardens because it's only 15 feet tall.

However, if you have the space, walnuts can grow 30 feet tall or more and almost as wide. They are a nutritious and beloved crop. However, a single tree would take up most of my yard, and its roots are allopathic, which means they could be hazardous to nearby plants. I love walnuts. My neighbors' backyard has a large stand of natural native black walnuts, which I've been trying to pick before the squirrels do, but it's difficult because the trees are so large.

Because of a disease, American chestnuts are all but extinct in the United States, but Chinese chestnuts can be found in most of the country, provided the winters and summers are cold enough. It is possible for Chinese chestnuts to reach 45 feet in height and width. You can coppice all chestnuts every few years and use the wood to build fences and posts, but you won't be able to harvest any nuts from the trunks. For centuries, pecans have been grown throughout southern states, including California. You'll need a lot of space if you want to put one of these in your yard. In the Midwest's frigid winters, shakbark hickory may be an option.

Oaks, in my opinion, is underappreciated as a source of food. Oaks may be found all across the world, and people have eaten them as long as they have been around. Tannin, which gives white oak nuts a harsh flavor but may be removed by repeatedly boiling or running water over them, has been reduced in newer types of white oak. My method for removing the ground nut meal is to place a tiny bit in a coffee filter and rinse until the water is clear.

Every year, I go to the hills and collect acorns from the local coastal live oaks, which I then crack ground, and leach to make bread and crackers. You get what you pay for in terms of flavor, and it's rewarding to connect with a real indigenous slow cuisine tradition in your area. Unless you own a large property, you should leave this tree in the forest, where it will grow abundantly, rather than bringing it into the garden.

CARING FOR FRUIT AND NUT TREES

Planting fruit and nut trees in the North is best done in early spring when rainfall can aid the root's growth. Autumn or even winter planting is possible in milder areas. Even if it's not practicable, you should prepare your soil the year before by adding mulch, compost, and a cover crop.

To get the best results from your trees and shrubs, start with healthy nursery stock. However, for citrus and other evergreens, you'll need to use container stock if you're planting dormant, bare-root deciduous trees early in the spring. Check out the roots if you're purchasing a tree in a container. Avoid plants with brown or root-bound roots; healthy roots should be white.

For a tree to be successfully planted in clay soil, you must ensure that it has adequate drainage. When it comes to trees that are particularly sensitive to poor drainage, seek rootstocks that can survive clay soil, such as avocado, citrus, cherries, peaches, and walnuts. Dig a larger hole than the rootball of the plant. Trees that are planted in holes that have smooth surfaces will not be able to spread their roots. The roots of the plant can forage for water and nutrients by slicing and breaking apart the sides and bottom of the hole. My preference is to use the native soil around the tree's roots instead of altering a planting hole. As soon as you've dug your hole, make a little mound of earth and gently drape the roots over it. To avoid crown rot and to allow for a mulch layer, place the plant a few centimeters above the surrounding soil (unless you are in an arid climate and planting into a mulch pit).

I make a doughnut shape around the base of the tree, approximately a foot from the trunk, by combining part of the natural soil with compost. Using this method, you'll be able to give the tree a good soak when you initially water it as well as keep the compost away from its base. If you need to water the pool on a regular basis, you can expand its size over time. To prevent compost and mulch from slowly moving downwards and building up at the base of your shrub or tree, lay bricks, urbanite (recycled broken concrete), or small logs uphill in a semicircle.

Pests

Many animals, birds, and insects appreciate the garden's abundance in the same way as humans do. However, the permaculture method begins by accepting that a portion of your harvest will be committed to the worthwhile cause of biodiversity rather than seeing pests as enemies of the garden. Beneficial species such as parasitic wasps, frogs, lizards, and snakes are attracted to a healthy, diverse garden and will take care of the majority of the natural pest control. With the help of habitats such as a water feature, rock pile, or pollination hedge, you may attract these creatures to your garden (for beneficial insects). Finally, you can use scarecrows, row covers, and even hand-picking to keep pests away from your crops.

Insects like moths, aphids, mites, and fruit flies love fruit. Sticky traps and pheromone traps can help reduce their population. If you use adhesive materials to band tree trunks and clay-based compounds (kaolin) to cover wounded trees, you can keep bugs from laying eggs. Pupation occurs on the ground for many tree pests. To keep pests at bay, be sure to remove any fallen fruit and trash from the ground beneath trees. The best way to ensure that your chickens are eating insects is to encourage them to peck around and beneath the trees. Weevils and curculios can be killed by tapping the tree vigorously so that the bugs fall to the ground and into a chicken's eager mouth.

Birds that feed on fruits and vegetables can decimate your harvest in a matter of days. Planting sour cherry trees (also known as pie cherries) has worked well for me because they don't appear to attract the attention of bird predators. Mulberries are often grown as a "sacrifice" crop for birds to consume by farmers. Reflective materials like old CDs and silver tape can be used to scare away the birds, as can decoy models of hawks and owls that are placed at a visible height. It is possible to design your own scarecrows. However, netting can be cumbersome to put up each year, making harvesting difficult; if birds are an issue, you may need to erect an enormous wooden frame several feet above the maximum height of the trees to keep them at bay.

It's not uncommon for four-legged animals like raccoons, chipmunks, and squirrels to be troublesome neighbors. There are numerous sites where deer are persistent and wreaking havoc, eating both food and attractive flora. Instead of perceiving bugs as a threat, some permaculture enthusiasts see them as a chance to catch or hunt some meals for themselves or their pets, interpreting the permaculture principle of producing no waste literally. There are other options available for people who aren't quite ready to make the leap.

Natural predators like coyotes, wolves, mountain lions, and snakes can help keep populations of squirrels and deer in check if you live in the country or near wild grounds. Keeping a pet cat or dog can help keep rats out of your house in a more residential situation (although a hunting cat is a danger to birds as well). Rats and raccoons can be effectively trapped, but traps can be dangerous for children and pets. Permaculture discourages the use of so-called humane traps because trapping and releasing pests elsewhere merely generates more problems for other people.

Pruning

Fruit trees in the permaculture garden should be pruned so that their fruit can be picked directly from the ground. Fruit trees should only be pruned to a height of 6 to 8 feet, according to Dave Wilson

Nursery, one of the nation's leading fruit tree growers. This type of containment pruning is most effective in the summer after the tree has produced its fruit. Pruning in the summer might slow down the tree's overall development and increase fruit bud production. When trees are dormant, winter is an ideal time for pruning since it allows for a better view of the entire structure, making it easier to remove dead or diseased wood and crossed branches. Pruning fruit trees in the winter encourages development in the following year.

Fruit trees can also be limited in size by espaliering, which involves growing a tree against a wall or fence. A south or west-facing wall can also be used to cultivate heat-loving crops like citrus or figs in borderline regions. There are numerous dwarf fruit trees that can be grown successfully in containers, but you'll have to remove and repot the plants every few years.

It's not just one type of fruit or nut tree that needs to be pruned, but typically each variety. Fig trees, for example, are pruned differently (white figs produce fruit from the previous year's growth, whereas black figs produce fruit from this year's growth). It is not necessary to prune many trees, such as persimmons and citrus. Others are doomed to failure if they aren't. Getting guidance from someone who has done this before is always a smart idea.

Grafting

In grafting, good fruiting qualities in an existing tree are combined with a desirable rootstock in order to produce a new plant. This is the reason why apples like 'Spitzenberg,' which were originally consumed hundreds of years ago, are being produced today. You may want to observe an expert orchardist or nurseryperson in order to learn how to graft successfully. Rootstock can be purchased from a nursery or grafted into an existing tree.

During the winter or early spring, depending on your last frost date, remove a pencil-sized piece of the scion (budded stem) from an established tree. If you don't want to get your hands dirty with a grafting knife, you can practice with a grafting punch. Cut the scion and rootstock with care so that they are the same diameter. Make sure the cambium layer (the brilliant green outer layer that covers the inner wood) is touching both the scion and the rootstock before inserting it into the keyhole of the cut rootstock. Rubber-band the graft and cover it with Parafilm (available at grocery stores) before sealing the bag. Keep your graft away from direct sunlight to keep it healthy. Water your grafted rootstock on a regular basis.

Remove the bag as soon as you notice buds on the scion of the graft. Remove the Parafilm and rubber bands after another six months. To get the most out of your grafted tree, you should plant it in the ground or move it to an even larger pot.

Layering

It is common practice to take a branch or shoot from the parent plant and bury part of it in the growing media (usual soil) while keeping it attached to the parent plant. Layering is a propagation technique. As soon as the shoot comes into touch with the soil, it will develop roots and be ready for transplantation.

Woody species such as fruit tree rootstock are commonly used for layering. Woody perennials like rosemary and lavender might also benefit from this method. Tips of branches from the current season can be buried in the soil to grow blackberries and certain raspberries.

It's a really straightforward process. To prepare the shoot for burial, clean off any leaves from the underside of the stem. A U-shaped stake or a rock can be used to secure the shoot in the ground. New plants can be separated from their parent plants after six months to a year of rooting.

Fruiting Shrubs

An elegant shrubbed foundation encircling a home in a suburban neighborhood is an old-fashioned landscaping staple. These are commonly used to create a sense of seclusion, although they don't

The Permaculture Gardening Bible: A Comprehensive Practical Guide to B...

add much more to the landscape. Permaculture advocates may want to consider replacing foundation plants around their homes with food-producing shrubs that also provide blooms, fall color, and screening.

In addition to these, blueberry, currant, elderberry, and gooseberry are all common food sources for shrubs in general. Elaeagnus multiflora, goji (Lycium barbarum), huckleberry (Vaccinium species), Cape gooseberry (Physalis peruviana), seaberry (Hippophae rhamnoides), serviceberry (Amelanchier species), and tree tomato are some of the shrubs that are worth trying (Cyphomandra betacea).

If you want to include edible plants in your food forest, it can be difficult to tell if they are officially a shrub or a vine, but that isn't the most critical consideration. Do not be afraid to plant what you like and what grows best in the given circumstances. The deer and the birds will enjoy the native fruiting shrubs in the outer zones of your garden, while you may maintain your cultivated varieties in zones 2 or 3 for easy harvesting (and netted, if need be).

Vines

The food forest's vines are the most adaptable layer. There are a lot of possibilities to use the edges and value the marginal and a method to layer edibles in otherwise wasted vertical spaces, thanks to these climbing or sprawling plants. A walk through a forest will reveal numerous examples of vines encroaching on other trees and spilling over their branches in order to capture any available sunlight. Nature does it, and so should we.

A building's front yard can be made more private with the help of vines. Training them to cover arbors and decks, attaching wires across a wall or fence to serve as a trellis, or even climbing up a building and covering the roof is possible. A building or an outside structure can be shaded or cooled by a grove of vines during the scorching summer months. It's possible to utilize the leaves of deciduous plants as mulch, and the vine's bare structure lets winter sunshine in. Be

151

realistic about how you want to integrate vines into your garden, and make sure you have a management plan in place before buying any.

Perennial Vegetables

To illustrate how permaculture is based on natural ecosystems, perennials are an excellent choice. It is only necessary to plant them once, and they will return each year. Soil disturbance is minimized once they have been established, and their extensive root systems help them draw water and nutrients from the deepest layers of the soil. Because perennials are among the first to sprout in the spring, they are especially useful when we rise from the lean months of winter.

These are plants that die back in the winter and then re-grow in the spring. Herbaceous perennials are the ones. After a long winter, asparagus and rhubarb are two of the most popular herbaceous perennial vegetables. Up to two months of asparagus can be picked from an established bed that is five years old or older. Despite the fact that the leaves of rhubarb are not edible, they provide a great deal of mulch or compost when they are thrown away.

The leaves of comfrey can be used to make chicken food, mulch, compost, and liquid fertilizer, making it the star of the herbaceous perennials. It can be simply spread by digging it up and breaking it into smaller pieces. Perennials must be planted with care because they will remain in the ground for a long time. Spread a layer of partially decomposed organic waste or sheet mulch around the plant each fall and amend the planting hole. During the winter, the organic matter will break down and enrich the soil, allowing the plant to better prepare for spring development. Early in the spring, before the active spring growth has begun, I also add completed compost in some cases.

Most perennials continue to develop throughout the summer and flower in the fall after their initial burst of growth in the spring. Keep them well-watered and mulched during the summer months to retain moisture and keep the weeds at bay around the plants. The seeds can be collected in the fall, when the plants are in full bloom, before cutting them back and disposing of the rest of the plant. Asparagus, artichokes, garden sorrel, purple coneflowers, and rhubarb all benefit from this method. The seeds of a small number of plants like tree collards do not set seed; thus, in winter-freezing regions, cuttings must be taken in the autumn and kept alive until the following spring as plants.

CHAPTER 11

PERMACULTURE SEEDING: GROWING VEGETABLES FROM SEED

Growing veggies from seed can be frightening if you've never done it before, but for the vast majority of vegetable crops, it's actually quite simple. It's as simple as starting with seeds, good potting soil, cell packs (small containers for seedlings joined together), sunlight, and a constant supply of clean, fresh water. You can save hundreds of dollars by growing plants from seed, and you'll be able to experiment with a larger variety of plants, including rare and heirloom types that aren't available as commercially grown plants. You don't have to worry about wasting anything when you grow your own food from seed, and you may think of your garden as a source of food for the following year.

Planting edibles in the ground is possible for many annual and some perennial edibles; however, cell packs can be a more efficient method of starting your seedlings. Because the seedlings are larger and stronger when grown in cell packs, they are more resistant to insects and birds than when grown in the wild. If you overseed rather than direct seed, you won't have to thin as many seedlings. Many warm-season crops can be started in a greenhouse or under glass in cold locations and then transplanted once the soil has warmed up and the threat of frost has passed.

DIRECT SEEDING

Carrots, radishes, lettuce, annual herbs, and salad greens are all good candidates for direct sowing since they have long taproots or mature quickly. Peas can be grown in the field rather than in a nursery, which saves time, money, and space. Large plantings benefit from the use of an Earthway seeder, which rolls around on wheels and can seed a bed in drills with seeds spaced anywhere from one inch apart to twelve inches apart. This eliminates the need to thin over-sown crops. However, precision planting isn't necessary for all crops. In addition to grains and beans that may be disseminated by hand, there are several other cover crops that can be used in this manner as well.

GROWING FROM STARTS

For seedlings, a greenhouse or a nursery table where you can watch and protect them from slugs or snails is the ideal location. Your nursery table can be in direct sunlight, indirect sunlight, or shade, depending on the type of crop you're growing. Ferns and other woodland natives, as well as delicious shade plants like French sorrel, shungiku (edible chrysanthemum), and nettles, are exceptions to this rule. In flats, I usually use eight six-packs, resulting in a total of forty-eight plugs. Plant seeds in tiny quantities unless you want to grow food on a large scale to sell or trade or if you want to give away starters to other gardeners.

Sow seeds in a sterile potting mix of high quality. Make sure you get the greatest quality organic potting soil you can find and then add 10% by volume of worm castings to it. Always mark your cell packs with the type of seed, the variety, the date, the source of the seeds, and any specific considerations. Start at the upper-left corner and work your way down, filling each empty cell with seeds (just like reading a book). For the most part, I use two or three seeds in each cell. You just need one or two seeds for large seeds like squash, while you may need three or four seeds for hard-to-germinate seeds like celery or cilantro. Having too many seedlings means additional labor because you'll have to trim them out.

Ensure that the seeds aren't buried too deeply by covering them with an additional layer of dirt and pressing down on them to ensure that they aren't exposed to air. Seeds should be sown as deep as their diameter. A bean seed can be put one inch deep, but a basil seed should be placed no deeper than one-eighth of an inch in the ground. If your seedlings outgrow their cell packs, make sure they have plenty of water and move them to larger containers. Pick a day with a high chance of clouds when you're ready to move them outside. Ensure that the young plants are adequately watered and protected with mulch, but don't suffocate them.

Seedballs

Pelletizing grains, wildflowers, cover crops like clover, and various vegetables in a clay-compost mixture known as seedballs is an option. Seedballs, also known as earth dumplings, was reintroduced by Masanobu Fukuoka, a Japanese chef and entrepreneur. They're simple to create and keep birds and rats away from your seeds. To make a ball of clay, simply combine three parts clay with one part compost, one part seeds, and a little water. Toss them in the garden after they've dried outside. The clay mixture will dissolve naturally in the rain, and the seeds will sprout on their own. If you're looking for a way to get your kids involved in some guerilla gardening, encourage them to make and spread sunflower seedballs in vacant lots or their own gardens.

SEED SAVING AND STORING

For millennia, people have been storing seeds in jars and other containers. The loss of seed-saving expertise in our culture over the past century has resulted in a considerable loss of biological variety. Indigenous people employed an average of 1200 plant species in pre-agricultural civilizations. Most of the world's population was fed by 1500 different plants in 1900. Currently, thirty distinct plants account for 90% of global food production, with three-quarters of that coming from only four crops: corn, rice, soy, and wheat.

Early twentieth-century crop diversity was 98 percent greater than it is today, making us more ecologically tolerant than we are today." At the cost of $1 billion, a single disease wiped out half of the South's corn crop and 15% of the national crop in 1970 in the United States, which was caused by a single gene. Landraces, or local types of corn, were discovered by plant experts in Mexico, the place where maize production began. They developed the next generation of hybrid maize with the disease resistance traits from the landraces they selected. There is a lesson here: learn from those indigenous farmers who wouldn't plant just one kind of maize. When it comes to preserving food, permaculture recommends the use of polycultures.

Why Save Seeds?

One of the best methods to implement permaculture is to save seeds. Learn to select the most productive crops from each year's harvest while saving money for future gardens through seed-saving techniques. When you share your seeds, you get to learn more about plants and meet people who share your interests. You should give seed saving a try, even if you're apprehensive at first.

Permaculture principles can be seen in the practice of conserving seeds. Seven thousand seeds can be found in one ounce of dried Kale or collard seed. This is an excellent illustration of a yield. How many seeds are in there? With so many seeds to save, you'll have to trade with other seed savers to assure a degree of generosity and to build community networks. Just think of all the greens you'll have grown if you share your seeds with others. Seed saving, polyculture, and watching natural cycles are only a few of the topics covered by Masanobu Fukuoka in his writings and lectures. It was difficult for visitors to his farm to locate his vegetable plots due to overgrown and fallow lands between his orchards. In the midst of the flora, Fukuoka was able to spot daikon radishes going to seed. Permaculture's roots may be traced back to natural farming, which emphasizes the significance of letting things go to seed and connecting the seasons.

It's easier to cultivate crops that are more resistant to pests and disease when you save your own seeds and plant them in your garden. Saving seeds allows you to select for certain qualities such as flavor, color, smell and texture, as well as form and juiciness. Saving heirloom seeds has the added benefit of preserving genetic variety, a proponent of environmental stewardship.

It's important to constantly save seeds from healthy plants with the required traits of a particular variety. Your message is clear: "I want more plants just like you next year." For example, if some lettuce plants are less likely to be eaten by slugs, leave them to go to seed so that you can replant them in the future.

Regional Adaptation

Seed storage methods and seed types vary by region. To produce a huge tomato such as Brandywine in my garden is difficult due to the lack of summer heat; thus, I choose to plant heirloom cherry tomatoes such as the 'Chadwick Cherry.' Distinct climates require different qualities, such as pest resistance or drought tolerance, short seasons or high elevation. Seeds that are resistant to diseases like early and late blight, for example, should be picked in areas with high humidity and significant rainfall.

The 'Chinese Giant' red mustard I saw during a recent cold snap was destroyed by frost on two of the plants, while the other two were unharmed. No question about it; seeds from the surviving were kept. Plants that are tough and tasty can benefit from the gift of natural selection when their seeds are saved.

Hybrids and Heirlooms

Your seed-saving attempts will be aided by gaining a rudimentary understanding of plant phylogenetics. Become familiar with the family, genus and species of the plants you are growing. Botanists have created botanical families to group together plants with similar floral designs and structures. One or more closely related genera can be found within each family (the plural of genus). Among the various plants in the aster, daisy, or sunflower family, the Asteraceae includes lettuce (genus Lactuca), marigolds (genus Tagetes), and sunflowers (genus Helianthus), all of which have composite daisylike flowers. Marigolds and sunflowers are unlikely to cross because they belong to different genera.

As indicated by the second Latin term, genera are further subdivided into species, such as Lactuca sativa, Tagetes patula, and Helianthus annuus (the sunflower). Plants of the same species, as opposed to those of different genera, do cross-pollinate. A plant is said to be true to type, and the seeds it produces are referred to as open-pollinated when two genetically related plants produce offspring that are identical to their parents.

A hybrid is a first-generation offspring of two plants that are genetically distinct. Large seed-breeding corporations manufacture the vast majority of them. Compared to their parent plants, these plants may be larger, more resistant to disease and pests, and more uniform in appearance. It takes thousands of plants to create a hybrid, and the ones that don't are rouged (killed off) since they lack the desired qualities. For the majority of home gardeners, breeding hybrids is a time-consuming and expensive endeavor.

Due to the fact that hybrid seeds do not produce offspring that are true to type, gardeners must buy new seeds every year when using hybrids. When it comes to seed saving, I advise against using hybrids (labeled hybrid or F1). The 'Sungold' cherry tomato, which has won numerous taste tests, was saved by me. I ended up with a 12-foot-long vine that produced bitter and thick-skinned microfruits. Hybrid plants are fine to grow but don't expect to be able to save seeds from them.

However, open-pollinated or heritage seed varieties have been grown for at least fifty years and passed down from one gardener to the next generation. We are carrying on this family legacy thanks to the seeds planted by our grandparents. While your open-pollinated seeds will result in plants that are extremely similar to their parents, your local environment will influence the plants' development.

Pollination

To germinate, grow, and flourish, a seed necessitates specific environmental conditions. While it may take some time for seeds to mature into plants, they will eventually self-replicate if left alone. An egg must be fertilized by sperm in order for human life to begin. Understanding how pollination works in plants will help you develop plants that are true to type.

It is not necessary for insects or wind to pollinate plants like peas and beans, which indicates that the male and female portions of each blossom fuse together. Seeds from self-pollinating plants are particularly simple to save, making them an excellent starting point for those new to the hobby of seed saving.

In addition to cross-pollination and wind pollination, there are two other methods that are a little more difficult. In order for cross-pollinators like squash to be fertilized, the seed saver needs help, which can lead to unexpected results. Insects like honeybees and flies transport pollen from the male flower to the female bloom in these plants, which have separate male and female flowers. It is difficult to successfully save true-to-type seeds when crops like maize are pollinated by wind, as the wind can carry pollen across long distances.

When it comes to most plants, you should store seeds from at least six separate specimens. However, if you have the space to grow more, then you should do so. In most small-scale seed-saving projects, corn is an exception. Without at least 200 plants, the next generation will have smaller ears due to inbreeding. For small plots of corn, hand bagging (in which a paper bag is stapled over the male and female parts and the tassels are brought in for pollination) is required.

Cross-pollination between plants of the same species is common, which is why knowing the botanical names of your plants is helpful. In the case of Brassica oleracea (Boissica, Cauliflower, and Kale), the cross-pollination of these plants may result in lovely vegetables this year, but the seeds of these plants may not be viable for future harvests. Physical barriers or timed pollination intervals can be used to keep the plants from interfering with one other. Ask your seed-saving neighbors to tell you what types they're cultivating so that you can avoid cross-pollination from neighboring plots.

Avoid cross-pollination by putting appropriate distance between your crops in large or multiple gardens. To separate, distinct plants from which you want to collect seeds, you can plant tall crops like beans, sunflowers, or other tall crops. Insects can't visit all of your crops at once and cross each other if you have a physical barrier in place. A house with a variety of plants planted on each side might also serve as a barrier. Alternatively, you might split your crops between your own garden and a communal plot. Rotating crops is a time-saver. Keep a seed rotation going by saving only one type of seed each year: kale for the first year and broccoli for the second year to avoid cross-pollination.

If stored properly, the seeds of most Brassica species can last for up to five years. Plantings can also be spaced apart in this manner. If you want to avoid the flowers of two different kale varieties clashing, grow 'Red Russian' kale early in the season and 'Lacinato,' for example, two months later. Isolation cages are also an option. Stapling row cover to a 1-by-2-inch wooden box frame is all that is needed to build your own cage. Make the cage large enough to accommodate multiple plants at once. Row-cover material can also be used to bag individual blooms or clusters of flowers.

PROCESSING SEEDS

Getting to the exciting part of preparing the seeds you've collected is always a pleasure. Plants can be classified as either wet or dry processing according to their family (although nightshade family crops like tomatoes have more nuances). Plants are normally allowed to bolt (bloom) and then produce seeds, which are dried on the plant. The seeds of some plants, like tomatoes, tomatillos, and zucchini, won't dry on their own and so necessitate wet processing. The seed-saving method is simple and straightforward once you get the hang of it.

Dry Seed Processing

There isn't much to dry seed processing. When the plants have dried out, you remove the seedpods or seed heads. When I was a novice gardener, I was delighted to discover that broccoli was producing vivid green seedpods filled with tiny green seeds. I was excited to show my mother where the seeds came from when she came to see me at the community garden I helped build in college. She informed me that I needed to wait until the seeds were more mature and dark in color before planting them. Most seeds won't germinate if you pick them before they've had a chance to mature.

You can learn how to detect when seeds are ripe by observing and engaging with them. Once they've become brown, the seedpods are easy to break apart with your fingers. You'll know it's time to harvest kale when birds start eating the seedpods, for example. When beans and peas are adequately dried, they should be able to be easily broken in half; if you try to break a bean in two and it's rubbery, it requires extra drying time. To dry unripe beans and peas with their roots still attached in climates with shorter growing seasons, they can be hanged inside a shed or flipped upside down.

Threshing and Winnowing Seeds

The seeds will need to be threshed when they have been dried further. Chaff (or seedpods or heads) are separated from their seeds during threshing. Set the seeds that will fall out of the basin on a sheet or blanket before you begin. In general, use your fingers to split large open seedpods, such as beans. The best way to warm up little seeds like kale is to gently rub them back and forth between your hands while holding a large bowl. Step on the majority of seed heads and rub them on a tarp to obtain bigger quantity of dried seeds.

Seed-cleaning screens are a must if you're serious about seed preserving. A garden supply store is a good place to get these, or you may construct them yourself. Using them for threshing and drying seeds is a win-win situation (and herbs, too). Seed screens are available in a variety of mesh sizes to accommodate a wide range of seed sizes, from the ultra-fine to the extra-large. A screen just slightly larger than the seeds should be used, with an even finer screen placed beneath them. Sift the seed mixture through the larger screen and into the smaller screen to remove any large pieces. In order to remove the dust, you'll need to select a screen just a tad smaller than the seed. Seed and a small amount of chaff, which is lighter than the seed, are all that is left after harvesting.

In order to separate seeds from chaff, the process of winnowing is used. While blowing gently on the seeds, transfer the mixture from one broad and shallow mixing bowl to another once the seeds and chaff have passed through the screen or have been freed from the hand-rubbed seed heads. The seeds can also be poured from one basin to another, and the chaff is blown away on a windy day. The bottom of the bowl will hold viable seeds while chaff blows away. Volunteer seeds will always spring up in your garden if you rake up the chaff. Composting the chaff is another option. Once the seeds have been whittled down to a manageable size, store them in a glass jar or envelope. Label the seeds with the date, variety, and any specific growing conditions that are relevant to the project. When you're ready to plant or give them to someone else, this information will come in handy.

Sunflower or daisy family (Asteraceae)

The sunflower family is an excellent source of seeds and attracts helpful insects, making it a win-win situation. Artichoke, Japanese burdock, cardoon, chicory, endive, lettuce, sunflower, salsify, shungiku, and yacon are all members of this diverse family. Only sunchokes, which must be started from tubers, are an exception to this rule.) Because lettuce plants self-pollinate, it is an easy seed to start with for a beginning seed saver. Wait until the plants are at their fullest potential and either bolt or develop a blooming stalk. Yellow flowers and white cottony seed heads can be found on some cultivars. It's possible to harvest lettuce seeds multiple times over the course of a few weeks because they don't all ripen at once.

Rub the ripe seeds off the plant with your palms and drop them into a supermarket bag placed underneath the plant. To remove the remaining chaff, winnow the seeds. Identify your seeds by including the variety, date, and place of origin on the label. Seed collection is even easier for large-flowered members of this family, such as sunflowers. Insects cross-pollinate the flowers. In late summer, remove the flower heads as soon as the seeds begin to fall off the petals. In a warm, dry place, place the heads upside down until all of the seeds can be easily rubbed off. Bag and label the seeds when they are completely dry.

Legume family (Fabaceae)

Garbanzos, lentils, cowpeas, and peanuts are all members of this bean and pea family. Because they are self-pollinators, they are among the most simple seeds for beginners to save (runner beans are an exception; they are pollinated by bees). Scarlet runner beans, in particular, excite my bean seed collecting hobby. It's like panning for gold for little pinkish red and sparkly black seeds when you take the generic bean pods and thresh them open. Thresh the peas or beans after they have ripened and dried on the vine for around six weeks. When the pea pods are dried and brown, you'll hear the peas rattling within when you shake them, and the Beans will turn yellow and dry out. In order to dispose of the pods, separate them from the seeds by breaking apart the pods. Treasure hunting with old wrinkled pods is a favorite childhood activity for kids. A burlap bag or pillowcase filled with beans or peas can be used to thresh them by continually stepping on them. In order to winnow a lot of beans, lay out two tarps and sandwich the bean pods between them. Then, tamp away until the beans are ready to be winnowed. Identify your harvest by noting the variety, date, and place of origin.

Peanuts are unique in that the legumes ripen beneath the surface. When the leaves turn yellow, it's time to dig up the whole thing. For many weeks, place the plants in a dry, warm location. They must be allowed to heal at their own pace. When ready to sow, remove the peanuts from the plant after a few weeks and keep them in the netted husk.

Onion family (Allium species)

White to purple biennial flowers from the onion family are exceedingly ornamental and can be found in the common chives and garlic as well as in the leeks, onions, and shallots. Due to the fact that they will not flower until the second year after winter, saving seeds is a bit more difficult in this case. You can start with seeds and conclude with seeds if you live in a warm winter environment and leave bulbing variety in the ground to grow seed to seed. During the winter, onions are stored in root cellars or non-freezing garages and transplanted in the spring. This is known as "root-to-seed" growing. It is at this point that the plants are able to go through the flowering stage and generate dry seeds.

Because the flowers of the onion family are unable to pollinate themselves, pollination must be carried out by insects and a number of other plants. Harvest the seeds when they have dried on the plant. Use seed screens, then winnow and bag and label your produce.

Goosefoot family (Chenopodiaceae)

For example, quinoa and spinach are part of this nutrient-packed family. You can let beets go to seed in the ground in mild winter areas. If you live somewhere with a harsh winter, you may have to dig up your beets and save the best ones in a root cellar, then plant them again the following spring. A single plant of spinach will never produce seeds since it is dioecious, meaning each plant is male or female. To improve the chances of pollination, aim to have at least six plants flower at the same time. Collect, thresh, winnow, and identify the seeds after they have dried on the plant.

Parsley or carrot family (Apiaceae)

Flowering plants in this genus are excellent at balancing the ecology because of their diversity. Insects of all kinds can be seen in abundance surrounding the flowers, and you can often witness small parasitic wasps devouring aphids. Carrots, celery, chervil, cilantro (coriander), dill, fennel, parsley, and parsnip are all members of the parsley family. Remember that Queen Anne's lace is a wild carrot relative and may cross with your garden's produced carrots if you have it nearby or in the garden at all. In order to prevent carrots from becoming woody and unusable due to genetic drift, you should save as much seed as possible.

Allow the plants to mature for a full year before harvesting the seed, as many parsley plants are biannual. If you live somewhere with a moderate winter, you can leave carrot plants outside to store seeds. Roots (stecklings) should be dug and stored in cold-winter locations, then replanted the following year. Even in cold-winter regions, parsnips are usually able to survive the winter on the ground. During the second summer, collect the seeds that sprout on umbels. Putting a paper bag on top of the umbel may be necessary to keep the seeds from falling out into the ground. Collect, thresh, winnow, and identify the seeds after they have dried on the plant.

Brassica family (Brassicaceae)

Greens in this resilient family include kale, mustard, radish and turnip, as well as several Asian varieties of watercress and broccoli. They are all members of the Brassicaceae family. None of the brassicas attract beneficial insects on their own. It is best to plant them in late summer or early fall so that they can survive the winter and generate seeds for the next year. If you plan to save seeds from your brassicas, be sure to separate the varieties and allow only one to blossom.

Arugula, radish, and watercress are good places to start if you only want to cultivate one type of each at a time. Broccoli and arugula cannot cross, and there are only a few cultivars of arugula. Once the blossoms have dried into brown seedpods, gather them and scatter them throughout the garden to encourage a new crop of arugula to grow.

Wait until the pods develop a light brown color before harvesting other brassicas. Because the seed is still immature, don't pick green pods. Alternatively, you can remove the entire plant and hang it in a warm, dry location until all of the pods are brown and ready to be harvested. Seed screens should be used before winnowing since brassica seeds are so small.

Grass family (Poaceae)

It's not just the grass family that has wind-pollinated grains, such as corn and barley. You don't have to be concerned about cross-pollination because most gardeners don't grow other grains. It's best to avoid cross-pollination with your neighbors if they're growing heirloom wheat at the same time as you.

If you save seeds from a corn plant, they are unlikely to be the same variety as the parent plant. To avoid genetic inbreeding, you'll need at least 200 corn plants, which isn't possible for most home gardeners. If you have a lot of lands and are willing to put in the time and effort, you can collect, thresh, winnow, bag, and label your own seeds.

Wet Seed Saving

For seeds embedded in the fruit's moist flesh, wet processing is the best option because they won't dry out on the plant. If left to decompose naturally, these plants would produce seeds that would germinate the next year. You can enable this fermentation to take place in a container with wet processing.

Nightshade family (Solanaceae)

Ground cherries, eggplants, potatoes, sweet and smoky peppers and tomatoes are all part of the nightshade family. The seeds of these plants can only be saved if the fruits are allowed to mature completely before being separated from the flesh. It is not uncommon for potatoes to be grown from underground tubers.

Start with the ripest tomatoes of your favorite kind if you want to store their seeds. A plastic container is required for each kind, and I use cleaned yogurt tubs for this purpose. To remove the seeds and pulp, squish the tomatoes into the container with your hands (you can use this to make salsa or sauce). To keep fruit flies away, place the container outside, out of the sun, and cover it with a towel. For about one week (depending on the temperature), let it sit until a white mold grows on the contents. It's a good thing since you're attempting to break down the gelatinous seed covering, and the fungus will do the work for you.

Rinse the container by emptying the contents into a sink. Pulp and non-viable seeds will float atop the fertile ones. Until the water is clear and the cleaned seeds are at the bottom, keep changing it. You can also use a seed screen or paper towel to air-dry the tomato seeds. You can put the seeds in a paper envelope or a glass jar with a few holes in the lid so that they can continue to breathe. Seeds need to be marked with the variety, date, place of growth, and any specific growing circumstances as the final stage.

Peppers, on the other hand, do not require the same kind of care. To remove the seeds, just cut open the ripe fruit and scrape them out with a knife. Wear gloves if handling a hot pepper is on your list of to-dos. Bag and label the seeds once they've been dried with a screen or paper towel. Tomatillos, on the other hand, are a breeze to grow. Blend the ripe fruit in a blender on low for a few minutes. Remove the seeds' watery pulp and discard it (you can make salsa or put it into soups). Removing all but the most viable seeds and pulp from the rest of the seeds and pulp is necessary; after that, dry, bag, and label.

Cucumber family (Cucurbitaceae)

Summer and winter squashes, gourds, luffa, and melons are all members of this family. Hand pollination is required for these plants. Tape up the male and female flowers at night, be sure to name the tape so you know which one is which the next day. Using a pair of scissors, cut off the male flower and remove its petals, exposing the pollen on its anthers the following day. Using a male bloom as a paintbrush, apply male pollen to the stigma of each female flower one by one. Each female flower should be pollinated by at least one male plant blossom. Retape the female flower after you've finished painting the pollen. It will develop into a fruit and produce seeds that are viable.

By scooping out the insides like you would for crafting a jack-o'-lantern, remove the seeds from the squash or pumpkin. A clean 5-gallon bucket should be used to collect all of the stringy material as well as the seeds and water. Leave it overnight. To get the best results, you'll want to separate viable seeds from those that haven't been sown. Dry, bag, and label the viable seeds after thorough rinsing.

CHAPTER 12

EASY STRATEGIES TO PROTECT YOUR PERMACULTURE GARDEN FROM PESTS

Pests that feed on plants are a common occurrence in vegetable gardens, but for most gardeners, they aren't a major problem. However, when pest populations reach an undesirable level, the little buggers can cause more than just a cosmetic inconvenience. The dangers of exposure to synthetic pesticides are becoming clearer to gardeners as they become more aware of the potential dangers of using them. Preventing pests from eating your plants in the first place is by far the most effective way to combat them. Pest control in your yard is easier than you might think if you follow the five simple steps I've outlined below.

STRATEGY 1: ENCOURAGE BENEFICIAL INSECTS

Pollinators are fantastic for the garden, but the beneficial insects I'm referring to are those that consume nuisance insects. As a natural pest control method, ladybugs, lacewings, minute pirate bugs, parasitic aphids, damsel bugs, and other helpful insects eat pests and shelter and feed their young. Predatory pests and nectar-rich nectar are necessary for the good bugs to come to your garden and feast on them. Insects prefer specific kinds of flowers as nectar sources, so don't expect any old bloom to do. To get nectar, they need a unique kind of floral architecture. If you have a lot of pest-eating benefits nearby, you're less likely to see a rise in pest populations. It's all about striking a decent balance between work and personal life.

STRATEGY 2: CHOOSE YOUR PLANTS WISELY

Pest problems are more common in some plants and plant kinds than others. It's not always necessary to use pest-resistant plants while trying to keep your yard free of pesky insects. 'Butternut' and 'Royal Acorn' are two of the most resistant types of winter squash to squash bugs. In the event, your potato crop is regularly defoliated by Colorado potato bugs. Other veggies may also be resistant to pests and diseases if you look for them.

STRATEGY 3: EMPLOY PHYSICAL BARRIERS

Physical barriers are one of the most effective strategies for preventing pests from invading your garden. A lightweight, spun-bound fabric that lays on top of or on wire hoops can be used to protect pest-prone plants. If you want to prevent pests from burrowing under the cover, leave plenty of slack and pin the sides to the ground. When I grow cabbage, broccoli, and kale, I use row cover to keep off invasive cabbageworm caterpillars from other countries. Aside from Mexican bean beetles, I also protect my young bean plants, my young cucumber plants, and my young squash plants against squash bugs and vine borers by using row covers. Remind yourself to take off the row cover once the plants begin to bloom so that pollinators can get to the blooming plants!

STRATEGY 4: UTILIZE INTERCROPPING

Increasing the variety of your vegetable patch might also help keep pests at bay. Pests may have a more difficult time finding their host plants if they are interspersed with a variety of vegetables, herbs, and annuals. Keep even modest monocultures out of the garden by growing a variety of crops in a variety of spots. The pest bug appears to be "confused" by intercropping, despite the fact that there is still much research to be done. Some bugs may need to land on a plant a certain number of times in order to locate and confirm that it is a suitable host. Inter-planting crops make it more difficult for pests to find their prey because they may land on a new plant type each time.

STRATEGY 5: GROW HEALTHY PLANTS

While it may seem like common sense, in this horticulturist's perspective, preventing pests in your garden is most vital. To put it simply, healthy plants are less attracted to pests because of their own immune systems, just like you and I have our own. Plus, pests are scared off by the plant's own chemical defense mechanism, which a healthy plant has plenty of. Your plants' ability to defend themselves against pests improves as their health improves. Make sure your soil is well-fed with organic matter before you plant your plants, and then place them in locations where they will thrive (sun plants in sun, shade plants in shade, etc.). One of the simplest ways to avoid pests from invading your garden is to cultivate happy, healthy plants.

Over time, you'll be able to achieve an ideal balance between beneficial and harmful bugs in your garden, and you'll have fewer pest outbreaks because of it.

CONCLUSION

Congratulations on getting to the end of the Permaculture Gardening Bible. It is important to understand that permaculture is a vast field. To aid you in learning more, this book is intended for people who wish to immediately start using permaculture concepts in their own lives. It is for those who desire to become self-reliant as well as improve their independence, self-sufficiency, sustainability, and perhaps even a group of like-minded individuals.

Everything about his book has been discussed from the viewpoint of an expert. I have been in the field, and I deem it fit to share my knowledge with you and help you achieve your dream of owning a permaculture garden.

Once again, congratulations on taking the decision to begin your own journey with permaculture garden. It is my belief that this book has been able to answer every question and cover every possible loophole concerning the concept of permaculture.

Now get started!

REFERENCES

Arora, D. (1986). Mushrooms Demystified. 3rd rev. ed. Berkeley, California: Ten Speed Press.

Christopher, S. (2013). The Vegetable Gardener's Guide to Permaculture: Creating an Edible Ecosystem. Timber Press.

Coleman, E. (1989). The New Organic Grower. Chelsea, Vermont: Chelsea Green.

Friedhelm, W. (2020). Permaculture for Beginners: Knowledge and Basics of Permaculture. Expertengruppe Verlag.

Hemenway, T. (2009). Gaia's Garden. 2nd rev. ed. White River Junction, Vermont: Chelsea Green Publishing.

Mars, R. (2005) The Basics of Permaculture Design. Chelsea Green.

Mollison, B. (1999). Introduction to Permaculture. 2nd rev. ed. Tyalgum, Australia: Tagari Publications.

Peter, B. (2012). The Permaculture Handbook: Garden Farming for Town and Country. New Society Publishers.

R. Mars, J. Mars (2008). Getting Started in Permaculture. 3rd rev. ed. White River Junction, Vermont: Chelsea Green Publishing.